Kris Niendorf

By *Leonard Gross*

How Much Is Too Much?

How Much Is Too Much?

The Effects of Social Drinking

Leonard Gross

A report on the greatest controversy over alcohol since Prohibition

Random House · New York

Library of Congress Cataloging in Publication Data
Gross, Leonard.
How much is too much?
1. Alcoholism—United States.   2. Alcoholism—Social aspects—United States.   I. Title.
HV5292.G7 1983   362.2'92   82-42809
ISBN 0-394-52726-7

Manufactured in the United States of America

98765432

First Edition

For M.G.

Contents

A Note
to the Reader

This book arose out of a personal concern.

I am a social drinker, and have been for thirty years. I love almost everything about drinking: the anticipation, the smell, the taste, the effect and the atmosphere it produces. Like most social drinkers, I'm mildly familiar with the consequences of overindulgence—the feeling that one's system has been unduly taxed and the guilt at having abused it—and, again, like most social drinkers, I've wondered at times if I was drinking too much and should cut back or stop altogether. But by and large I've been a careful drinker: nothing during the day or after dinner except on special occasions, just a cocktail or two before the evening meal, and a beer or glass or two of wine with it. I've almost always used alcohol as a means to a pleasant transition from the workday to a relaxed evening, and I've been comforted by the knowledge that many doctors have recommended moderate drinking as a safe way to ease tension.

A few years ago, however, I began to notice a disquieting addition to the reports that various medical societies were issuing to the public on how to avoid a variety of diseases. Buried among the recommendations at the end of these reports was a caution to drinkers of alcoholic beverages not to exceed more than one or, at most, two drinks a day.

Almost none of my drinking friends drank in such a manner; for them, three to five drinks a day was the norm. All of them perceived themselves as "social drinkers"; none of them, to my knowledge, had ever experienced professional or social or personal problems as a consequence of their drinking. But could it be that these people were unknowingly endangering their health? Was I?

I decided to find out—if only for my own benefit—just what "moderate" drinking was, and how much one could safely drink without forfeiting the social, psychological and even the physiological benefits of alcohol. Considering that the overwhelming majority of persons who use alcoholic beverages view themselves as "moderate" drinkers, it would seem like an obvious question, and had a direct, authoritative answer been readily available, I would not have undertaken this book.

No such answer was readily available. The subject, I soon learned, was so obscured by a jungle of trade-offs, so complicated by conflicting evidence and, at times, so encumbered by emotions that scientists were skittish about calculating a bottom line, let alone proposing one for public consumption.

I take a different attitude, one formed a quarter of a century ago when, as a reporter for *Collier's*, I journeyed to Denver to interview a scientist who for a number of years had been at work on a study of the human life cycle. I knew that this scientist and his colleagues had already learned a great deal about life-enhancing habits; it was my job to persuade them to share this knowledge with the public. No, the scientist said, they couldn't do that; their study was the life cycle and they were not about to reveal their findings until many more years had passed. The response struck me as hubris. "My wife is pregnant," I said to the scientist. "Are you telling me that you have information that might benefit our child but are going to withhold it?"

My argument won the scientist over, but he was less successful with his colleagues. Whatever information they had never would benefit our children. From that time on, my attitude has been that scientists, so much of whose research is supported by public funds, owe it to the rest of us to share their knowledge. Never mind that the findings are imperfect, or incomplete. Tell us what you've learned and list your caveats so that we can at least make an intelligent choice.

That principle, it seemed to me, had never been more applicable than it was to the question of social drinking. I was some months into the hunt when, pushed to the edge of patience by too many too-careful answers, I heard myself demand of a major figure in alcohol research, "How much can I safely drink before I begin to encroach upon certain areas of risk such as cancer, heart disease and liver disease? How much can I safely drink without impairing my intellectual capacities or taking years off my life? Given the state of the art, what is the best course for a person to follow? I think these are fair, legitimate questions, and I feel that the people who work in the field of alcohol ought to be willing to respond. If there's a danger, I want to know about it, and if I can drink with impunity, I want to know about that, too, because I love to drink."

This time I got my answers—qualified, but answers. In the process I also discovered a story that, as one social epidemiologist put it, had largely passed beneath the surface of public view.

Fifty years after the end of Prohibition, there is—to borrow Theodore H. White's incomparable phrase—fire in the ashes of the issue that had once set this country ablaze. What has stirred the ashes, as we shall see, is the question of whether the problems associated with alcohol abuse are in the bottle or in the man. For years following Prohibition, that was the forbidden question. Science, commerce and alcohol treatment groups structured an uneasy peace around the proposition that man himself was the problem. But now that proposition is being vigorously challenged from a number of directions. Implicit in the counterproposition that the problem might lie in the bottle —at least to some extent—is the question of when that problem begins. Are alcoholics and other heavy drinkers the only ones at risk or are social drinkers affected as well? That is the fundamental question of this book.

But fundamental questions invariably give rise to others, and those questions, too, are taken up in this book: Why do we drink? What benefits does drinking yield? How does the context in which we live affect the drinking that we do? Why do some people seem to be more vulnerable than others to the effects of alcohol? Do social drinkers delude themselves about the amounts of alcohol they drink? What is addiction, and at what point does it begin? Does a daily craving for a couple of drinks mean that one is addicted? And what of "relative risk"? If, in fact, social drinking is more hazardous than imagined, what are the odds? Do they or don't they favor the social drinker? And if the odds are unacceptable, how can one improve them? Is there a safe way to drink?

The field of alcohol research may be rife with factionalism, but no one would dispute that there has been an explosion of knowledge in recent years about drinking and its aftermath. Few of the above questions are being answered today in the same way they were twenty and even ten years ago. Nor is scientific concern about drinking and its aftermath confined to the United States; it exists in many countries whose populations drink. My questions, accordingly, had to be put to alcohol researchers not only in the United States, but in Canada and Europe as well. Throughout, my objective has been to assemble a report that would enable social drinkers—myself included—to maximize pleasure and minimize risk.

How
Much Is
Too
Much?

1 · "How Come Nobody Ever Said Anything?"

Not long ago, six middle-aged Manhattan-based business-men flew to Florida to sail a sloop back to Newport, Rhode Island. During the week that they tacked up the Atlantic seaboard, the crew abided strictly by the conventions prohibiting alcohol on board ship in deepwater sailing. As they came into harbor, their minds to a man on the gin-and-tonics they would soon be hoisting in celebration of their successful journey, one of the six demanded, "Can any of you guys remember the last time you went a week without a drink?" Not one of them could.

In the United States today, 70 million habitual users of alcoholic beverages are in the same boat with those sailors. Social drinking may run second only to television watching as America's favorite pastime, and the two habits are mutually reinforcing. Each year the alcoholic-beverages industry spends half of its almost billion-dollar advertising budget on beer and wine commercials advancing the proposition that social drinking may lead to relaxation, fellowship and even sex. It is hardly a new proposition; what *is* new is the degree to which social drinking has permeated our society. Alcohol is consumed today by more people on more occasions and in more places than at any other time in history.

On December 5, 1983, fifty years will have passed since the United States Congress approved the Twenty-first Amendment to the U.S. Constitution, repealing the eighteenth article of amendment. The Eighteenth Amendment, ratified on January 16, 1919, had made it illegal to manufacture, sell or transport intoxicating liquors within the United States, and to import or export them as well. In the years since that unfortunate attempt to legislate social custom, a conventional wisdom in regard to the pros and cons of drinking has gained such acceptance that it is embraced by, among others, the liquor industry itself: alcohol, taken immoderately, can be a killer drug. The abuse of alcohol costs the nation billions of dollars annually in lost or diminished productivity, poor health, medical expenses, crime and its prosecution, traffic accidents and deaths, and social welfare. But much or most of this cost, the industry goes to great pains to point out, is associated with a small minority of problem drinkers—those reputedly incurable alcoholics who, because of some genetic or biological quirk in their systems, shouldn't drink at all. For the overwhelming majority of the drinking population, alcohol is proclaimed as the ally it has been for most people through the ages, a beneficent adjunct to life, a social lubricant that eases stress, melts difficulties and even contributes to good health.

The idea that alcohol, used in moderation, enhances health has a long history and appears to be periodically reaffirmed even in contemporary studies, some of which indicate that moderate drinkers live longer than either alcoholics or abstainers. Of the many hypotheses about the source of this putative benefit, the most popular currently is that moderate drinkers profit from a better supply of a blood protein that reduces atherosclerotic deposits in the arteries, thereby reducing mortality by heart attack (heavy drinkers may get this salutary effect, too, though other, more serious consequences of heavy drinking may outweigh it). At its extreme, alcohol's salutary benefits have given rise to quite liberal conceptions of safe drinking limits.

But this expansive view of "moderate" alcohol consumption is, unfortunately, not the entire story. Within the last decade, a number of researchers in the United States and abroad have been evolving another, totally contradictory proposition: what passes for social drinking today in many parts of the world is so fraught with biomedical hazards that it could be exposing millions of self-described "social drinkers" to serious health hazards. Among the risks these researchers cite:

- An increased danger of liver problems
- An increased danger of hypertension
- An increased danger of cancer of the digestive tract
- The possibility of serious side effects for those drinkers taking other mood-altering agents or even prescription and over-the-counter drugs
- The possibility of fetal damage even before a pregnancy has been confirmed
- The impairment of sober intellectual capacities

All of these possibilities have been amply reflected in recent reports to the U.S. Congress by the National Institute on Alcohol Abuse and Alcoholism (NIAAA), a government agency created in 1971. The third such report, called *Alcohol and Health*, issued in 1978, contained a warning unmistakably directed at social drinkers: "The countless ways we integrate alcohol into our lives—from the college beer bust to the cocktail party to the drinks before, during and after dinner—must be examined critically by millions of people. People must become conscious of when, where, why, how much and how often they drink —and the corresponding risk they are assuming."

On all such assertions the alcoholic-beverages industry casts hostile and suspicious eyes. It perceives them as manifestations of a comprehensive program mounted by an "anti-industry cabal" and "neo-Prohibitionist cadre" that is "trying to roll back the clock." "They have an agenda," Paul Gavaghan of DISCUS (the Distilled Spirits Council of the United States, Inc.) declares. On that agenda, he maintains, are attempts to influence research, to affect the course of the NIAAA, and eventually to curtail the supply of alcohol through higher taxes, restrictions on advertising, the reduction of retail outlets and compulsory labeling of alcohol products with a Surgeon General's warning, similar to the one carried on cigarette packages, about the possibility of risks to health.

Beginning with its 1978 report, the NIAAA had adopted a standard that identified anyone consuming two or more drinks a day on the average as a "heavier" drinker. The industry, for its part, absolutely refuses to categorize drinkers into "light," "moderate," and "heavy." It argues that body weight, genetic factors and even varying cultural perceptions about what constitutes heavy drinking make the answer different for each individual. That much all researchers concede. But, say its critics, the industry uses this argument as an excuse not to address the issue of biomedically safe drinking limits, per se, and to deny that biomedical risks might exist for any but the heaviest drinkers. This, the critics contend, isn't true, and as a case in point they cite recent diagnoses of cirrhosis among persons drinking amounts few drinkers would regard as excessive.

Cirrhosis is a disease in which the liver becomes so scarred that the patient doesn't have sufficient healthy tissue to perform the organ's critical functions. The problem with cirrhosis is that unless you're getting regular medical checkups you don't know you've got it until you have it—and once you have it you've "bought the package." A frequent question one liver specialist, Dr. Charles Lieber of New York, gets from his dismayed patients, many of whom consider themselves social drinkers, is, "How come nobody ever said anything?"

How come nobody ever said anything? How is it that the possibility of a connection between social drinking and biomedical risk has not been made more forcibly? One reason is that the association is still so new and tentative that it is the focus of intense debate. Another reason is that Americans seem to compare so favorably to other cultures when it comes to drinking. The amount of pure, or absolute, alcohol consumed in the United States in 1978, the last year for which figures are available, was 2.82 gallons per capita. Per capita consumption in Portugal is approximately 6.2 gallons of absolute alcohol, more than twice what it is in the United States. France (5.9), West Germany (3.9), Switzerland (3.7), Italy (3.6) and a number of other countries all exceed U.S. per capita consumption.

A final reason for lack of attention to the possible hazards of social drinking is to be found in the *modus vivendi* that his existed almost since the end of Prohibition between the manufacturers of alcoholic beverages on the one hand and those people who study and deal with alcohol-related problems on the other.

2 · The Strange Bedfellows

From a public health standpoint, Prohibition had been a qualified success. Mortality rates from cirrhosis of the liver, the disease most commonly associated with heavy alcohol consumption, had dropped significantly. Alcohol-related hospital admissions had fallen, and with them, alcohol-related violent deaths. But the social costs had also been considerable as criminal elements vied with one another to profit from an insatiable demand, and breaking the law became a way of life for millions of otherwise circumspect citizens.

In the aftermath of Repeal, no agency of the federal government wanted to touch the issue of alcohol consumption. Federal involvement in that issue had been perceived by a generation of Americans as a disaster, and the political cost of further involvement was simply too high. Public health authorities, especially, recalled with pain the damage to their cause, and they did not wish to be perceived, once again, as "reactionaries."

Most subdued of all, perhaps, were the alcohol researchers. They wanted to put as much distance between themselves and the temperance movement as they possibly could. Alcohol, that movement had vouched, could, by its ability

to injure cells, damage all of the body's organs, even the unborn child in the mother's womb. In the 1940s the prevail-
ing scientific viewpoint was that the damage of alcohol was
indirect, occasioned more by malnutrition, squalid living
conditions and other frequent corollaries of heavy drinking. Accordingly, among researchers there was a tendency
to minimize rather than amplify the physiological problems
associated with alcohol consumption, and one eminent
epidemiologist even went so far as to publish an article
arguing that evolution rather than alcohol was responsible
for cirrhosis. The degree of self-censorship practiced by
the researchers can only be imagined. As Robert Straus,
chairman of the department of behavioral science at the
University of Kentucky's College of Medicine and one of
the deans of alcohol research, put it, "It is interesting to
conjecture whether the need of scientists to dissociate from
the temperance ideology and from being labeled as 'drys'
may have profoundly influenced the questions that scientists were asking, thus precluding the discovery of answers
that were then socially undesirable, and significantly de-
laying many of today's most important discoveries." Whatever the cost, the world of alcohol research was eager to
present a calm and modest face to the American public.

Out of the quiet a proposition finally emerged that enabled the researchers, the federal agencies and the professional agencies in the field of alcoholism once again to find
voice: the problem of alcohol was not in the bottle; it was
in the drinker. There was nothing wrong with the substance; there *was* something wrong with a certain small
minority of drinkers who, for some mysterious reason,
could not drink without harm to themselves and eventually
to others.

That mystery became the focus of most research in the
field of alcohol studies. It was a research activity that met
the unqualified approval of the alcoholic-beverages industry.

Few were pointing accusing fingers at its product any longer; the finger wagging was directed at those individuals who could not and should not drink.

What came to be called the "disease concept" of alcoholism has by now dominated the field for more than thirty years with scarcely a voice raised in protest. The *modus vivendi* served the industry on the one hand and the alcoholism treatment establishment on the other, and it persists to this day. "The uninitiated might think (and rightly) that this is a strange bedfellowship, indeed; but it is the logical outgrowth of a community of interests," Don Cahalan, a co-author of *American Drinking Practices,** a bible of the alcohol-research field, wrote a few years ago in the *British Journal of Addiction.* "The liquor industry naturally would like to stave off all attempts to constrain the sale of alcoholic beverages, so they try to focus public attention on the individual-person 'disease' aspects of alcoholism, intimating that those not born with the disease may drink 'moderately' (undefined) without risk of disease. Thus they make common cause with the leaders of the National Council on Alcoholism and related associations, who would like to see practically all of the available public funds spent on treatment of the unfortunate crop of present alcoholics, probably because most of these agency leaders come from the ranks of Alcoholics Anonymous."†

But by the mid-1960s, three related factors had caused many alcohol researchers to become restless with this *modus vivendi.* The first was that the generation of Americans most closely associated with Prohibition and its disruptive social aspects had passed away. This meant that any concern expressed about alcohol problems, particularly by the public health sector, would not automatically be tarred

* New Haven: College & University Press, 1969.
† Volume 74, 1979, pp. 235–238.

with the temperance brush. A second major factor was a sudden upturn in per capita alcohol consumption, reflecting a similar rise in most countries of the Western world. While the rise in the United States could be explained to some extent by the entry of women and young persons into the drinking population, for the most part it was due to increased consumption by traditional drinkers. The explanation for the increased intake might be nothing more complex than affluence; an increase in disposable income had apparently enabled millions of drinkers to indulge their desire for more alcohol. Whatever the explanation, researchers profess to see a correlation between increases in general consumption levels and increases in the number of heavy users. An increase in the number of heavy users, in turn, means an increase in problems associated with alcohol. At a certain point, such problems can no longer be ignored.

A third important factor contributing to the refocused concern over alcohol abuse was the rise of the drug problem generally in the mid-1960s as a major national issue. Marijuana, LSD, heroin, their use made popular by young people revulsed by the Vietnam war, aroused and alarmed parents throughout the country. "I have no way of proving this, but I think what happened was that a lot of congressmen who were upset with their kids fooling around with marijuana went home to dinner and got their Scotch bottles thrown in their faces," speculates Ron Roizen of the Alcohol Research Group at the University of California, Berkeley.

Willy-nilly, the problem of drinking followed on the coattails of drug problems in general, so that by the time a Nixon Administration bill proposing the establishment of a federal agency to study alcohol problems appeared before Congress in 1970, Congress was ready to pass it.

Public Law 91-616, sponsored by Senator Harold Hughes

of Iowa, a recovered alcoholic, provided that a National Institute on Alcohol Abuse and Alcoholism (NIAAA) would be established for the treatment and rehabilitation of alcoholics. Strangely enough, the creation of the federal agency was not so much an attempt to create an awareness of alcohol problems as it was an effort by professionals in the movement to legitimize the disease-concept notion. What better way to do that than to create a federal agency? But what the professionals in the alcoholism field expected from the NIAAA is not what they eventually got.

At the outset, the NIAAA adopted a viewpoint that the alcoholic-beverages industry would find congenial to its interests. This view reflected the ideas of the NIAAA's initial director, Morris Chafetz. Chafetz's notion was that moderate drinking could serve as an insulation against problem drinking. Teach people to drink moderately, his argument held, and you will solve the problem of alcohol abuse. As models, he offered the Italians and Jews, ethnic groups that integrated spirits into household life, that had low rates of alcoholism and to whom the idea of drunkenness was anathema. "*Shikker iz a goy*," the old Jewish ditty held— "The Gentile is a drunkard." By way of affirming the notion that the answer to the problem was to encourage drinking in socially controlled settings, the NIAAA could point to a study done under its auspices by psychologist Richard Jessor of the University of Colorado, a respected social scientist who has worked extensively in the field of alcohol research. The study demonstrated that Italian youths who migrated to Boston had far more problems with drinking than did those youths who remained in Italy.

Chafetz's own explanation of the low rates of alcoholism found among Italians and Jews was borrowed from alcohol anthropology. He drafted into service the idea that a culture with a coherent set of norms and ideas about drinking would have low levels of problems, while a culture that was ambivalent about drinking—one that harbored heavily charged and contradictory views about alcohol—would produce high rates of alcohol problems. The solution, as he saw it, was to convert the culture from an ambivalent to a nonambivalent one. Tracts against alcohol were to be discouraged because they only recharged the issue and further heightened its ambivalence. Nor were abstainers to be held up as models, because their abstention was based to a great extent on an irrational loathing of alcohol. The key to a coherent policy was "responsible drinking."

If Chafetz's program was one the liquor industry could live with, it was too "wet" for the Alcoholics Anonymous constituency, which looked to the NIAAA for its advocacy and legitimation. What was wanted, this constituency held, was a director with a biochemical background who could get the NIAAA back to basics. If the central tenet of the alcoholism movement was that alcoholics are biochemically different from normal drinkers, didn't it make sense to have as a director a biochemist who could focus research on that problem?

But while a biochemist might be expected to study the general pathway of alcohol through the metabolism, that sort of research could prove to be quite heretical. Once you turn to the biochemical community to start researching what you want, they soon begin to wonder how you can have anything like responsible drinking if you have a substance that can do what alcohol does. It's inevitable that they will get interested in the chemical consequences and the metabolic cost of alcohol per se.

That is exactly what has happened. An inquiry into the biochemical consequences of alcoholism has led researchers to a consideration of alcohol, the substance. In the process, the biochemists have opened up a whole series of questions regarding drinking at less than alcoholic levels—the theme of which is that consequences might exist for social drinkers as well.

Ironically, it was the man the alcohol-treatment community singled out to legitimize the disease concept who, instead, put the agent of that disease under the research microscope.

3 · A Heretical Proposition

Ernest P. Noble is speaking, a trim and fastidious biochemist, and psychiatrist as well, with jet-black hair though he is past fifty, a small mustache, and a speech pattern that faintly echoes an Armenian ancestry and a youth spent in Baghdad:

"The major emphasis at the time I came to the NIAAA was treatment. The emphasis was primarily on the individual, the diseased individual, the suffering alcoholic. There was very little in terms of prevention going on, let alone effective prevention. Most efforts that were called prevention were public announcement spots—'Alcohol is a disease . . . call us if you're in trouble.' Eighty percent of the budget of my institute was going for treatment, very little of it was going to research and even less was going to prevention efforts. So I felt that we had to rectify that situation. I began to look at prevention efforts around the world, and came up with the notion that in order to contain the problem we had to look at the public health model of alcohol problems. The public health model states that there are three critical components to every problem: the host, the agent and the environment. We were dealing only with the host. The environment was given lip service, and the agent, alcohol, was completely ignored. So I felt that in order to be effective, we had to bring in the two other issues, and at that point I began to say, 'Hey, you've got to look at the agent itself. Without alcohol you don't have the problem.' Now, it seemed that that was a very new concept for the country to deal with."

Noble combines the bird-dog tenacity of a researcher with an accessible and engaging manner. It is this combination, perhaps, that has made him at once the most controversial and the best-liked man in the field of alcohol research. "I can't think of anybody I've ever known who's more honest and forthright than Ernie Noble," one admirer effuses. Noble is also highly regarded in the field, even by those who disagree wholeheartedly with his objectives. Says an opponent: "I haven't seen a piece of research by Ernie Noble that I haven't respected."

It was Noble's own research into the effects of drinking on cognition that largely shaped his career as well as his attitudes to alcohol. His studies convinced him that even small amounts of alcohol could adversely affect an individual's ability to think. The finding so impressed him that he altered his own drinking habits. For years his regimen had been the same: a cocktail before dinner, a glass of wine with his meal and a cordial after dinner. Today Noble has one or two glasses of wine, usually diluted, with dinner once or twice a week, but only on those evenings when he has no important business the following morning. He never drinks at a business lunch, although he used to do that, too. At the monthly seminars at the University of California, Irvine, where Noble initially reported his findings, it had always been the custom to maintain an open bar; as the professors became more and more familiar with the implications of Noble's work, patronage of the bar began to dwindle and it was soon abandoned altogether.

Much of the research into the potential health hazards of drinking at less than alcoholic levels was initiated during Noble's two-and-a-half-year tenure as director of the National Institute on Alcohol Abuse and Alcoholism. To the alcoholic-beverages industry, it was a stormy and shocking and contentious time, and it is widely believed that Noble's abrupt ouster as director was due primarily to industry pressures on the Carter Administration.

Today Noble occupies the Thomas P. and Katherine K. Pike Chair in Alcohol Studies at the University of California at Los Angeles—the first endowed chair of alcohol studies in an American university—pursuing once again the work interrupted by his several years in government. That work, and its evolution, provides an excellent pathway to an understanding of how and why alcohol research has come to concern itself with social drinking.

Noble's interest in the field arose from his initial inquiries into the biological basis of brain function. He had begun professional life as a biochemist, working primarily on cancer and leukemia. But he found the work frustrating because he didn't have the same access to patients that medical doctors did. So he decided to become a physician. It was during his residency at Stanford that his interest turned to psychiatry as well as the influence of alcohol on the brain. He knew that alcohol damages the brain of chronic alcoholics, but he didn't understand the biochemical basis of that damage. Working with animals, he discovered that small amounts of alcohol impeded the synthesis of protein and RNA molecules in the brain. The result raised an immediate question: If alcohol can cause such damage in animals that are not addicted to alcohol, can it also cause damage in humans who are not addicted to alcohol?

From a research point of view, it was a new question. All previous studies on alcohol and the brain had dealt with alcoholics. No one had thought that the extensive brain damage they experienced might apply to a lesser degree to social drinkers, and that they, like alcoholics, might experience significant loss in their powers of cognition—their memory, abstracting ability and ability to conceptualize.

Inherent in Noble's question was a heretical notion: that perhaps alcohol the drug was causing a problem independent of the disease state of addiction.

After Stanford, Noble pursued his research at the University of California at Irvine. In 1974 he took a sabbatical leave, moving to Strasbourg, France, along with several of his graduate students, to study the effect of alcohol on cells. In the midst of his work he received a telephone call from a friend in the United States. The director of the NIAAA, Morris Chafetz, had resigned. Would he be interested in the job?

"Are you crazy?" Noble countered. "I'm a professor in a fine university. I get a fairly good salary, I've got a nice place to live in California. Who wants to go into the bureaucracy?" But two other friends called, urging Noble to apply for the job. After discussing the matter with his wife, Noble allowed his name to be put up for consideration, and almost overnight he was chosen to be the new director of the NIAAA.

His first act after taking office in 1976 was to visit every NIAAA field program in the country. He returned to Washington thoroughly depressed by the scope of alcohol abuse. Not only did it pervade all segments of society, it was not decreasing. The NIAAA, in its six years of existence, had managed to set up treatment centers and hospitals throughout the country, but to little avail. "Maybe we're not getting at the source of the problem," Noble suggested to his colleagues.

Until that point the NIAAA, the brainchild of a recovered alcoholic, had been saying, in effect, "The problem of alcohol abuse is one caused by the genetic weakness and abnormal metabolism residing in the individual, who for reasons we can only suspect at the moment cannot tolerate alcohol." For Noble to propose that the substance, alcohol, might be the source of the problem was to raise, once again, the forbidden notion that had precipitated Prohibition.

The liquor industry and the alcoholism-treatment movement responded as one. Charges of neo-Prohibitionism filled the air. "What are you trying to do?" one critic demanded. "That didn't work during Prohibition. Why bring it up again?"

He was not out to promote Prohibition, Noble argued. It was simply that his own research, plus the research of others in the United States and abroad, was suggesting more and more strongly that drinkers did not have to be dependent on alcohol to develop consequences from it. Among those consequences were cirrhosis, gastritis, hypertension, cancer and a measure of brain damage. He was convinced, if only as a researcher, that society had to look at alcohol as an agent that could cause many of these problems—not sufficient by itself, perhaps, but without which the problems might not exist to anything like the degree that they do. To the question "When does a person become an alcoholic?" he would respond, "When does a cucumber become a pickle?" What was clear to him, and what he began to say publicly, was that alcohol, taken in sufficient quantity, was a poison. "Alcohol is the dirtiest drug we have," he would argue. "It permeates and damages all tissue. No other drug can cause the same degree of harm that it does. Not even marijuana, heroin or LSD, as dirty and dangerous as they are, are as pervasive in the damage they cause as alcohol."

It was just at this point that Noble found an issue to dramatize his concerns—the possibility that expectant mothers risk injuries to their unborn children by drinking during pregnancy. For some time he had been reading reports of this so-called fetal alcohol syndrome. Most of these had been animal studies in which a dose-response relationship seemed quite clear; the more alcohol the animals were given, the more damage their fetuses incurred. Now it was being suggested that the same thing could happen in humans. Noble convened a conference of top scientists from around the world to evaluate the evidence. What emerged from their discussions was a conviction that an expectant mother didn't have to be an alcoholic—as had previously been supposed—to injure her unborn child. Drinking at much more modest levels could cause harm as well.

Following this finding, the NIAAA issued a warning to expectant mothers to curtail their drinking to no more than two drinks a day. It was more than a specific warning; it was the introduction, on an official basis, of the notion that the alcoholic is not necessarily the only one who gets harmed by alcohol.

A corollary to that notion was that the safety net strung by the national government had to be large enough to catch the nonalcoholic problem population as well. Part of that net, to Noble's thinking, had to be a prevention program aimed at stabilizing the level of consumption so that the problem at least didn't get worse. He came under the thrall of a theory, with origins in France, to the effect that limits on the availability of alcohol would diminish the problem drinking population.

During the first year of Noble's tenure he had received polite treatment from the alcohol industry, which perceived him as a laboratory man who would concentrate on research and treatment. The strategies Noble had come to espouse were an entirely different matter: curtailing the supply of alcohol through higher taxes and higher prices, restrictions on advertising, the reduction of retail outlets and a strong public education program on the possible hazards of drinking for nonalcoholics.

Advertising was a particular target of Noble's. He felt strongly that the portrayal of alcohol in the media was causing young people to start drinking at an earlier age than they otherwise might, encouraging present drinkers to drink more and persuading abstainers to become drinkers.

"If we're going to bring about a change in our country's attitudes," he counseled his colleagues, "we have to get at the way people think about drinking." What he proposed to do was attack the widely held public assumption that only those drinkers "damned by the gods" could become alcoholics and all the rest were immune.

Even those who admire him most believe that Noble's attack was naïve. "What he was doing was buying the concept that if you're able to reduce the amount of drinking X percent, you could lop off the top of the scale of heavy drinking," Don Cahalan suggests. "That flies in the face of common sense. If you tax alcohol, you're going to drive out the light drinkers. The heavy drinkers are going to pay more and more and more."

What may also have been naïve was Noble's belief that the increasing support he was gaining from certain segments of the alcohol establishment would be sufficient to carry the day. He did not seem to realize at the time just how much of a threat he posed to the alcoholic-beverages industry.

By 1979 Noble was gone, the victim, to some, of those two "strange bedfellows." As Don Cahalan wrote in the *British Journal of Addiction*: ". . . we have seen within the last year an enormous hue and cry on the part of a coalition of the U.S. liquor industry and many of the leaders in the alcoholism treatment movement to detach the scalp of Dr. Ernest P. Noble . . . on the grounds of neo-Prohibitionism . . . Dr. Noble is an internationally recognized research scientist who was naïve enough to believe that one might proceed logically to do something to limit alcohol consumption, in view of the high correlation between alcohol consumption and alcoholism. He was fired within a few months after the controversy first erupted, ostensibly over policy differences with his new boss, who was appointed after Jimmy Carter was elected, although the likelihood is high that Noble would have weathered these differences if a coalition of alcoholism associations and the alcohol industry had not been aligned against him."*

"Ernie took his mission seriously," one researcher said recently. "He thought he had a mandate to at least keep alcohol problems at their present level." What he accomplished may ultimately prove to be infinitely more important—enlarge the perception of the problem to include millions of drinkers who did not previously come under the "problem" purview.

For years the social problems associated with heavy drinking—family disruptions, falling down on the job, violent behavior—controlled the discussion of alcohol problems in this country, and the cost of alcoholism was calculated in those terms. "The result," says Robin Room, director of Berkeley's Alcohol Research Group, "has been a real downplaying of the question of physiological complications of drinking, which is much more of what middle-aged and middle-class folks are at risk of. If alcohol was like tobacco, where all you have to worry about is the long-term physiological consequences, there would have been a lot more emphasis on those consequences than there's been."

If recent history tells us anything, it is that the time for that attention is at hand. "Research into social drinking is the coming thrust in alcohol," says Richard Bast, director of special research for the NIAAA's National Clearinghouse for Alcohol Information. "It's winning the attention of more and more researchers." Noble adds, "That's where the crunch is. The whole field of alcoholism is contentious in its own right. When you get into the area of social drinking, you get even more contention."

Which is to be expected. Contention is alcohol's birthright.

* Volume 74, 1979, pp. 235–238.

4 · The Contentious Drug

"You have asked me how I feel about whiskey," a Mississippi state senator told his legislature in 1958. "All right, here is just how I stand on this question:

"If, when you say whiskey, you mean the devil's brew, the poison scourge, the bloody monster that defiles innocence, yea, literally takes the bread from the mouths of little children; if you mean the evil drink that topples the Christian man and woman from the pinnacles of righteous, gracious living into the bottomless pit of degradation and despair, shame and helplessness and hopelessness, then certainly I am against it with all of my power.

"But if, when you say whiskey, you mean the oil of conversation, the philosophic wine, the stuff that is consumed when good fellows get together, that puts a song in their hearts and laughter on their lips and the warm glow of contentment in their eyes; if you mean Christmas cheer; if you mean the stimulating drink that puts the spring in the old gentleman's step on a frosty morning; if you mean the drink that enables a man to magnify his joy, and his happiness, and to forget, if only for a little while, life's great tragedies and heartbreaks and sorrows, if you mean that drink, the sale of which pours into our treasuries untold millions of dollars, which are used to provide tender care for our little children, our blind, our deaf, our dumb, our pitiful aged and infirm, to build highways, hospitals and schools, then certainly I am in favor of it.

"This is my stand. I will not retreat from it; I will not compromise."

Throughout history, mankind has looked upon alcohol with the same double vision as that Mississippi legislator, although rarely with as much good humor. "Who hath woe?" the Bible asks. "They that tarry long at the wine . . ." But the Bible also says: "Wine . . . maketh glad the heart." Among the Greeks, wine was so popular that Socrates spoke out against its overindulgence, and Plato recommended a number of measures to curtail supplies and consumption. In the early days of Rome, drinking was discouraged, and women, servants and everyone under thirty were prohibited from drinking altogether; not until the second century before Christ did drinking become so widespread that women were reveling as openly as men. Drinking was common among the Aztecs, but a man who got drunk could be sentenced to death. "Three glasses of wine can set everything to right," according to an ancient Chinese proverb, but public officials were prohibited from drinking in the capital to prevent them from becoming drunk, local laws prohibited the making, selling and drinking of alcohol, revelers were subject to heavy fines, and manufacturers to loss of property, slavery and even death.

In 1983, fifty years after the end of Prohibition, the United States continues to look at alcohol with the same double vision.

On the surface, we seem to be a drinking country. More Americans of drinking age drink than don't. Drinking is powerfully associated with holidays and celebrations, and the use of alcoholic beverages is widely encouraged through conspicuous advertising campaigns.

And yet, when it comes to the consumption of alcohol, the United States is really two countries, one wet, the other dry. "Wet America" consists of the Northeastern and Pacific states; "dry America" encompasses the Southern, Prairie and Mountain states. In "wet America," restrictions on the consumption of alcohol are virtually nonexistent. In "dry America," die-hard custom can make it tough to get a drink. That, however, doesn't stop millions of its residents from drinking.

The two different traditions in regard to alcohol have put some deep cultural imprints on the two "countries." Inhabitants of "wet America" tend to drink with relative decorum but have a higher rate of disease associated with the consumption of alcohol than do residents of "dry America." "Dry America" has twice as many abstainers as "wet America," a low per capita consumption and only half as many heavy drinkers, but an extraordinarily high rate of social disruption associated with such drinking as exists. Serious drinkers in "dry America" are something of an embattled Good Old Boy subculture on the wet side of a rigid moral boundary between drinkers and nondrinkers.

Within recent years, consumption in "dry America" has risen much more dramatically than in "wet America." While overall consumption in "wet America" is still much greater, drinkers in the South and other dry areas, who twenty years ago consumed the same amount of alcohol as their "wet America" counterparts, are now drinking 30 percent more.

The moral here appears to be one that not only emerged from Prohibition but has persisted through the centuries: the tougher you make access to alcohol, the more determined some drinkers become to get it.

"The abuse of alcohol has been recognized as a problem in the civilized world for thousands of years," notes Frederick L. McGuire, a professor at the University of California, Irvine, who specializes in the effects of alcohol on behavior. "Its continued use is known to be associated with an early death, deterioration of vital organs, brain damage, diminished sex drive, poor hand-eye coordination, blindness, tremors, poor memory, divorce, loss of job and friends, physical and mental abuse of infants and other innocent bystanders, death on the highway, airplane crashes, suicide, rape, murder and a host of other 'unwanted events.'

"In spite of such statistical, experimental, and clinical evidence, man has continued to expend great effort and ingenuity in order to obtain alcohol. He has learned to make it by fermenting potatoes, rice, fruits, dandelions, barley, corn, cactus, and a variety of other substances, and to process it by heating it in fancy copper vats as well as in a sheet metal tub hidden in a pine forest. Attempts to halt this flood of harmful booze have met with great resistance, including uprisings against the law, gangster killings, economic chaos, and produced almost as much human misery as the alcohol itself. In spite of the fact that large numbers of people are not afflicted with alcohol-related problems, the persistence of the problem is awesome and all-pervasive; the use and abuse of alcohol can almost be described as an instinct, a social-biological urge often as strong as sex or aggression."

What is this combination of "devil's brew" and "philosophic wine" that is so capable of producing such double vision both in the societies in which it is used and in the individuals who use it?

Alcohol is an accident of nature. Fermentation—or conversion to carbon dioxide and alcohol—is caused by a reaction between yeasts and sugars. It happens in barley, which yields beer; in apples, which produces cider; and in grapes, which creates wine. To make stronger spirits, such as whiskey, gin, vodka or brandy, requires a process called distillation, in which a substance is first vaporized and then condensed.

Ethyl alcohol is the basic ingredient of all whiskey, wine and beer. It is combined with various kinds of "congeners," which give each beverage its distinctive taste, and with water.

The amount of alcohol in the mixture is expressed by its "proof," but you must divide the figure by two to get the true proportion of alcohol to water. An 80-proof gin, in other words, is 40 percent alcohol. The remainder is essentially water.

French wines, which generally range between 10 and 12.5 percent alcohol, tend to be less alcoholic than California wines, many of which are 13 and 14 percent alcohol. Beers, too, have different standards; in some states 4.5 percent beer is sold, in others only 3.2 beer is allowed. "Light" beers are those whose alcoholic content has been diluted still further.

The same ingredients that go into the preparation of methyl, or wood, alcohol (which is used in antifreezes, paint removers and solvents for shellacs and varnishes) and isopropyl alcohol (which is used in disinfectants, rubbing alcohol, after-shave lotions and window cleaners) are also used in the preparation of ethyl alcohol, or ethanol, as it is known in the trade. Ethanol is used in the preparation of antiseptics, solvents, cough syrups and beverage alcohol.

Because methyl, or wood, alcohol converts to formaldehyde in the body, it can be poisonous when either ingested or inhaled, even in small amounts. Ethanol, which converts to acetaldehyde, can be poisonous too if a great amount is consumed in a short space of time. The Addiction Research Foundation of Toronto estimates that 10 to 13 ounces of ethanol—approximately 20 to 26 ounces of 100-proof whiskey—would be fatal for an adult of average weight if consumed in less than an hour.

The extraordinary fact about ethanol, however, even though it is a poison when ingested in such large quantities, is that it is not poisonous when taken in small amounts over protracted time periods. That is the key to alcohol's success.

Alcohol affects every part of the body, but what attracts people to it is what it does to the brain, the computer of their nervous system. Psychiatrist William B. Terhune once likened the brain to the central office that receives, records and returns messages, and the spinal cord to the cable through which those messages pass, via nerves, conducting the stimuli between brain and body. "The nervous system is similar to an automatic-dial telephone installation," he explains. "The cells of the central nervous system are very sensitive to those drugs which are able to reach them. The specific effect of alcohol on nerve cells is to dissolve the fat, increase cell fluids, and make the cells temporarily inactive. Every time you take a drink you are putting some of your brain cells temporarily out of commission. Indeed, if alcohol did not have that effect, you would never drink it."*

Let us trace a drink through the body to show how this occurs.

Within minutes after you have swallowed your first sip, you can feel the alcohol spreading from your stomach to your extremities. The observable sensation is surprisingly accurate. The alcohol passes into the bloodstream from the stomach and small intestine and then to the heart, which pumps it to the rest of the body. It's when alcohol reaches the brain that the pleasurable effect takes place, to be followed by less pleasurable effects if sufficient quantities are drunk.

All of these effects are a consequence of the amount of alcohol in the bloodstream—the blood alcohol concentra-

* *The Safe Way to Drink.* New York: Morrow, 1968.

tion, or BAC. The BAC is measured in milligrams of alcohol per 100 milliliters of blood, or milligrams percent. In most states a person is considered legally intoxicated if his BAC is .10%. The potency of alcohol as a drug can be appreciated best if one understands that .10% means one part alcohol to 1,000 parts blood.

"Because the brain and spinal cord contain a high concentration of blood, it is understandable how alcohol can so readily affect cognitive, emotional, and motor functions," Professor McGuire explains. While the states recognize .10% for legal purposes, most consider .05% as a blood alcohol concentration at which a person is likely to endanger others while operating a vehicle, and recent studies have found visual acuity affected at doses as low as .02%. "The overwhelming majority of accidents involving alcohol are not accidents in which tracking is the prime error," says UCLA professor Herbert Moskowitz, a ranking authority in the field. "Contrary to what most people think, it isn't that people are weaving down the road, which is a sign of very high blood alcohol levels, it's that they have failed to see something. They go through a red light, they fail to see a pedestrian or a motorcyclist, they fail to see that the road is curving. Their perceptual and attentive mechanisms are affected very early, after just one drink. These are the things that are the prime causes of accidents and, unfortunately, these are the kinds of impairments that are not self-obvious; you don't know you don't see something when you don't see it. When you stumble and you can't walk well, that you see and can work on trying to correct. But the greater the effort to correct, the more likely you are to fail to see important elements of the environment that lead to the more serious accidents."

At a blood alcohol concentration of .05%, says Moskowitz, the driver has increased his accident probability by 100 percent over driving without any alcohol in his blood.

At .10%, the accident probability has increased by 600–800 percent, and at .15%, by 2,500 percent. These percentages, he stresses, are not just applicable to traffic accidents, but to accidents of all kinds.

Flying while under the influence of alcohol has become a considerable problem in recent years. A graphic idea of what elevated BACs can do to flying skills can be seen in the results of a 1972 experiment in which eight professional and eight nonprofessional pilots were tested at levels from .04% to .12% as they took off and landed under instrument conditions. At the lowest BACs, the professional pilots committed procedural errors that were considered hazardous, and at the highest level their flying was so erratic that the safety co-pilot took the controls eleven times to avoid accidents. The nonprofessional pilots did even worse, particularly on procedural tasks: they took off with full flaps, flew without lights, turned the wrong way and attempted to land on instruments while tuned to the wrong radio frequency.

"Not only is actual performance affected by alcohol, but the perception or judgment of risk is affected," McGuire states. He cited a study in which professional drivers were asked to drive a bus between two rows of posts with varying distances between each set of posts. As their BAC levels increased, the drivers were prepared to navigate ever more narrow gaps but needed wider gaps to succeed. At .04%, three of the drivers were ready to take the eight-foot bus through spaces as much as fourteen inches too narrow.

Findings like these have made McGuire a conservative on the subject of drinking and driving. "Most tests of performance designed to test skills relevant to the driving situation are seldom as complex as the actual driving tasks," he argues. "The danger posed to life and limb by relatively low blood alcohol levels is grossly underrepresented. The fact that most persons are not so affected is little comfort if that small percentage of the driving population is driving your car or is sharing the highway with you at high speeds and at close quarters. Careful reflection . . . gives increasing respect for an argument that no one should be allowed to drive even if he has had only *one* drink."

Other countries, McGuire asserts, consider the United States rather backward in its relatively soft treatment of drunk driving. "In San Salvador drunk drivers can be shot (fortunately, they have very few automobiles). In South Africa the penalty is ten years in jail and a $3,800 fine. In Turkey, a drunk driver is often taken 20 miles from home and forced to walk back. In Australia the drunk driver's name is listed in the local newspaper in a column with the headline, 'He's drunk and in jail'; .08% is taken as evidence of intoxication, and the guilty party is subject to a $600 fine and six months in jail. In Great Britain, Switzerland, Austria, and France, a BAC of .08% is taken as presumptive evidence of driving under the influence, while in Norway, Iceland, Poland, and Yugoslavia it is set at .05%. The lowest levels exist in Czechoslovakia, Bulgaria, and East Germany, where .03% will lead to conviction; in fact, the Czechoslovakia law states that no one may operate a motor vehicle after having anything to drink . . ."

Blood alcohol concentrations don't diminish rapidly; they can remain high for hours after drinking has stopped, and a small amount of alcohol added to them several hours later can shoot them back up again. The man who has one or two drinks in the club car on his way to Connecticut several hours after a three-martini lunch in Manhattan may have a BAC above the legal limit when he steps into his car for the drive home from the station. Alcohol may even be present in the blood in the morning following a heavy night of drinking; more than one driver has been charged with drunk driving on his way to work in the morning, even though he's had nothing since the previous evening.

· · ·

The amount of alcohol one requires to reach each successive BAC level depends on a variety of factors. The first of these is body size; if a 100-pound woman and a 200-pound man, each with the same drinking histories, drink the same amount of alcohol at the same rate, the woman will feel the effects more quickly than the man simply because the alcohol, traveling through her body in the bloodstream, passes through a smaller cell mass. She also has less blood with which to dilute the alcohol.

A second factor affecting BAC is the competition. Alcohol taken on an empty stomach has a much greater effect than after you've eaten. In the latter case the alcohol is competing with bigger, more assertive food molecules for passage through the membranes of the stomach and small intestine, and often loses out.

The third factor is the type of alcoholic beverage ingested. Generally speaking, the higher the alcoholic content of the beverage, the more quickly the blood level rises. Thus a straight whiskey has the greatest kick of all, followed by fortified wines like port and cream sherry, table wines, beer and cider.

A fourth critical factor is the rate at which one drinks. Two generous dry martinis, drunk in half an hour, can bring the drinker close to the point at which it is illegal to drive. But, theoretically, a person could drink at a rate so slow that he would feel none of alcohol's effects, even if he drank throughout the day. "If someone is drinking an ounce of absolute alcohol in half an hour, that's a considerable difference compared to someone drinking an ounce over four hours," James Beard, director of the Alcohol Research Center at the University of Tennessee's College of Medicine, declares.

What actually happens to the body as a consequence of drinking is something that goes completely counter to one of the most widespread myths—that drinking causes dehydration. The myth is based on two immediate effects of the ingestion of alcohol. First, it acts as a diuretic, increasing the formation of urine. Second, it acts as an astringent on the mucous membranes of the mouth.

In terms of the long-range effects of drinking on the body's water supply, both immediate effects are deceptive. The rate of water loss from the body does increase when one drinks, but only as long as the blood alcohol increases. Once the blood alcohol peaks, plateaus or falls, the process of diuresis not only stops but actually reverses. The formation of urine is reduced, and the body stores water at a greater than normal rate. That process is known as "antidiuresis."

The explanation is a simple one. The body contains an antidiuretic hormone, which alcohol inhibits, but only as long as the blood alcohol level is increasing. Once the process reverses, the hormone is released, and water is retained. (If one eats peanuts, pretzels or potato chips while drinking, the extra quantities of salt reinforce the process. Even though the body is losing water as the blood alcohol rises, the kidneys retain the salt. Once the water loss has stopped, this greater-than-normal supply of salt acts further to retain water.)

The consequences of antidiuresis are easily ascertainable to anyone who has drunk a little bit too much the night before. All he need do is try to remove a ring or make a fist to determine how swollen his hand is, or feel how unusually tight his shoes are, or feel that unpleasant throbbing in the head. All of these phenomena occur because of increased water in the body's cells, which causes them to swell. That throbbing head, the most common unpleasant aftermath of indulgence, may be due to nothing more than an increase in pressure due to an extra quantity of water in the cells.

The final factor affecting the amount of alcohol in the bloodstream is the rate at which the body metabolizes what has been drunk.

Only a small portion of alcohol—2 to 5 percent—is eliminated in the urine, breath, saliva and sweat, although these percentages can rise when large quantities of alcohol are consumed in a short space of time. Even so, more than 90 percent of the alcohol consumed must be converted by the body through metabolic processes.

This quantity of alcohol is metabolized—that is, broken down and burned—at a more or less constant rate. If the rate at which you drink is greater than the rate at which you metabolize, higher rates of alcohol begin to accumulate in the blood.

It's the liver that is mainly responsible for metabolizing alcohol. The liver is the largest organ in the body, weighing three to four pounds. It is located on the right side of the abdomen, behind the lower ribs; everything leaving the stomach and intestines passes through the liver en route to other parts of the body. In passing, conversion occurs, which is why the liver is known as the body's refinery. It converts food to chemicals; manufactures enough bile each day to help us digest our food; detoxifies and excretes poisonous substances; and processes drugs absorbed from the digestive tract into substances the body can handle.

The liver has surprising quantities of an enzyme that is the agent of the metabolic process. It is called alcohol dehydrogenase, and its presence is "surprising," as psychiatrist Donald Goodwin suggests in his book, *Is Alcoholism Hereditary?*,* "because, as far as we know, alcohol dehydrogenase does nothing except metabolize alcohol. It is there in all mammalian livers—in the horse's in particular plentitude. Why? Did God anticipate that someday a mammal like man would develop a taste for alcohol and need a way to dispose of it? Or did it happen that millennia ago horses and other vegetarians ate fermenting fruit lying on

---

* New York: Oxford University Press, 1976.

the ground and their obliging livers evolved a helpful enzyme?"

The liver detoxifies alcohol by oxidizing it, a few drops at a time, into other, detoxified chemicals. Even though the liver is the primary site for the detoxification of alcohol, it is extremely vulnerable to alcohol and its metabolic by-products, especially acetaldehyde.

A liver worn out from everyday duty in rendering alcohol innocuous will not perform as efficiently as one that's fresh at the job—a circumstance that brings us to certain alcohol-related phenomena of concern to every habitual drinker. These phenomena are *tolerance, dependence* and *addiction*, and all of them relate to a fairly discouraging fact of life: as the signal-giving ability of the liver wears down, the habitual drinker must consume more and more alcohol over the years in order to recapture those agreeable euphoric feelings.

"In lay terms alcohol tolerance is described as that phenomenon in which one person 'holds his liquor' better than another; in other words ingestion of the same amount of alcohol by the tolerant person induces fewer psychomotor effects than in the average," Dr. Thomas B. Turner, of the Johns Hopkins Medical School, noted in a recent book. "Tolerance is customarily considered to be acquired by exposure to alcohol, in contradistinction to accumulating evidence that individuals may vary in their natural or initial sensitivity to alcohol, which may be associated with in-born factors." One of the in-born factors, Turner points out, is that all adults, whether they use alcohol or not, produce an average of three quarters of an ounce of absolute alcohol in their bodies each day, which the liver metabolizes. In reality, then, all humans, even abstainers, are constantly exposed to alcohol and deal with it with varying degrees of efficiency. Habitual, or chronic, drinkers, says Turner, "develop substantial tolerance to alcohol which permits them to perform at levels of efficiency not possible for the nontolerant person." A social drinker having two to four drinks a day will develop some degree of tolerance within days or weeks.

"Viewed from one important aspect, the presence of tolerance tends to mitigate and blunt the intoxicating effects of alcohol," Turner notes. "Probably, the sum of these effects among the drinking population is very great, particularly in that portion in which moderate drinking is the rule." In one sense, this is a blessing, because younger and presumably less alcohol-tolerant drivers have much higher rates of alcohol-related accidents than do older, presumably more alcohol-tolerant drivers. Driving experience, per se, could be a factor, but the fact is that chronic, alcohol-tolerant drinkers have demonstrated an ability to perform all sorts of motor tasks at varying degrees of intoxication that are impossible for "naïve" drinkers.

Unfortunately there is an aspect to the development of tolerance that is not a blessing, as Turner himself acknowledges. "Tolerance also probably has adverse effects, in that it may lead indirectly to higher levels of consumption to achieve desired effects, intake levels which may prove to be physically damaging . . . perpetuation of the psychotropic effects of alcohol may require increasing amounts of alcohol, which in turn may lead to dependence."*

"You know," a friend of thirty years said to me, "I simply had to acknowledge a long time ago that I have a certain specific need for alcohol. I want a drink at the end of the day." She always has at least one drink, she admitted, and as the years have passed, it's been more like two and sometimes even three. There's usually a glass or two of wine with dinner as well.

Certain alcohol researchers who study such matters believe that the consumption pattern and the concerns of my

* Henke Rigter and John C. Crabbe, Jr., *Alcoholic Tolerance and Dependence*. New York: Elsevier/North Holland Biomedical Press, 1980.

friend are mirrored in the patterns and concerns of at least one in five American drinkers. The usual form of such concern is the simple, encompassing question of whether the person is drinking too much. There is a widespread feeling —even a conviction—on the part of such drinkers that they have developed a dependency for alcohol that borders on addiction, if it isn't addiction altogether, and many of them wonder if they have become incipient alcoholics. If they don't, their families often do. G. Alan Marlatt, a professor of psychology at the University of Washington (and the co-author of some stunning new research on drinking behavior which we'll see in the next chapter), tells of a man who has been drinking four to five glasses of wine each day for the last several years. His wife—whose father was an alcoholic—feels that her husband has become alcohol-dependent, and is pressuring him to stop drinking. He's put in the position of having to hide his wine bottle, which she then finds and measures. The experience leaves him with feelings of guilt—which, according to the literature on alcoholism he reads, are an indication that he may be an alcoholic.

"A lot of the behavior that people get into is not because of any dependency but because of reactions to social disapproval," Marlatt states. "They're in that gray area between the people who drink very occasionally, and those who are dependent upon alcohol. Everything they read about alcohol tells them that they're in one of two camps: either they're in the camp that's filled with problem drinkers and alcoholics, or else they're in some completely safe camp where they drink only once or twice a week. These people drink every day, and on the average anywhere from three to six or seven drinks. Most of them are worried. Most of them ask, 'Does this mean I'm dependent on alcohol?' "

Most alcohol researchers would say yes, but vary considerably in the seriousness with which they view the problem. Dr. Turner defines physical dependence as "a neurochemical alteration in the body from continued alcohol ingestion." A reduction in alcohol intake can trigger a reaction in the dependent person "which may vary in its intensity from mild restlessness to life-threatening delirium tremens," but the withdrawal syndrome rarely develops at alcohol intake levels below six drinks a day for the average-sized person.

Professor Robert Straus, the behavioral scientist at the University of Kentucky, identifies three different forms of dependence on alcohol. The first is physical dependence, in which the tissues of the body become so accustomed to the presence of alcohol that the individual feels ill without it. The second is psychological dependence—what alcohol researcher Kaye Fillmore has called "an American drinking norm"—in which the individual relies on alcohol to alter his mood, particularly in special situations: a trip, a weekend, as a prelude to sex. The third form is what Straus calls "social dependence," in which the individual drinks because the situation demands it. "Since situations that prescribe drinking as appropriate permeate our society," Straus observes, "people with lower than 'normal' capacities for alcohol are frequently faced with social expectations that they drink 'too much.' To the extent that they feel a need to comply with social expectations for drinking what for them is 'too much,' they are manifesting a dysfunctional social dependence on alcohol."

If social drinkers feel uncomfortable when deprived of alcohol, should they worry about it? "That's in the area of things we don't know about," Straus responds. Others are not so charitable. "One definition of alcoholism (a rather satisfactory one clinically) is 'loss of power of choice,'" Dr. Max Hayman noted in an article called "The Myth of Social Drinking."* "I would suggest—even challenge—

---

* *American Journal of Psychiatry* (November 1967).

the social drinker to stop drinking and observe his own feelings of loss and dependency, his rationalizations and, so frequently, a return to old habits of drinking. This can be an excellent gauge of one's dependency on alcohol."

The question implicit in Hayman's challenge is at what point "dependency" becomes "addiction." That, among alcohol researchers, is a matter of grave dispute. To some, the craving for alcohol may be nothing more than the individual's desire for a pleasant reward at the end of a hard day, a period of "time out," as psychologist Craig Mac-Andrew and anthropologist Robert B. Edgerton call it.* To others, it is the telltale sign of loss of control. The one theory on which both sides might agree is that addiction begins when drinking creates problems for the drinker and the drinker keeps on drinking even though he himself is aware of the problems.

The social and psychological problems associated with drinking are multiple and usually obvious, if not to the drinker, certainly to those around him. The physical problems are not generally obvious—at least not the chronic disorders that result from long-term, persistent drinking at levels that can produce the problems. That brings us to another potential problem associated with the consumption of ever larger quantities to attain a "buzz" or "high." As you adapt to the intoxicating effects of alcohol, you become less and less adept at judging how much you should drink. You may feel you can handle more with no ill effects, but that extra load it takes to give you the feeling you're seeking could be toxic to your system.

The body can burn off only so much alcohol. The most common yardstick used is one drink an hour, but that overstates the case. The average-sized man can metabolize only about ¾ to 1 ounce of whiskey or 8 ounces of beer an

* *Drunken Comportment.* Chicago: Aldine Press, 1969.

hour, each less than a conventional "drink."* What aggravates the situation is that very few drinkers nurse a drink at the rate of one per hour.

It's that excess that makes a person "feel" his drink. It's that excess that works on the body's cells. When the body's cells are confronted with the same assault day after day, the cells rebel, and illness results.

But only in some people.

Winston Churchill drank a bottle of brandy every day of his most effective years, functioned brilliantly and lived to be ninety-one. Everyone knows someone who drank heavily but never became ill and lived a long and rich life. Why is it that such people can drink and get away with it, while others shorten their lives? How is it that one person can drink to his satisfaction every day of his life and not live a day less than his allotment, and another, drinking in the same manner, dies ten years before his time? Consider a population of 1,000 persons. If no one in that population drank, they would experience no alcohol-produced diseases. If all of them drank six drinks a day, only a certain percentage of them would develop alcohol-related problems. Why them, and not the others?

People vary in the sensitivity of their organs. A person may be more liver-sensitive than brain-sensitive; it's not uncommon to have cirrhosis of the liver diagnosed in someone who says, "That's impossible. I've never been drunk in my life."

We've seen that the manner in which the liver can

---

* The formula is 100 milligrams per kilogram per hour. A person weighing 70 kilograms (154 pounds) would metabolize 7,000 milligrams —exactly 7 grams—in an hour. A smaller person would metabolize less, a larger person more. Thus, a 100-pound woman (45.45 kilos) would metabolize 4.5 grams, and a 200-pound man (91 kilos) would metabolize 9 grams an hour. So, in reality, very few drinkers are capable of metabolizing as much as one full drink an hour, particularly if the drink is of generous size.

metabolize alcohol depends to a great degree on its condition, but the size of the liver is another important factor. And quite apart from wear and tear due to drinking, the inherent efficiency of each liver may vary as well. No two are exactly alike, just as there are no two automobile engines alike even though they are constructed back to back on an assembly line. Livers might have microscopic differences in structure that would become significant only at certain levels of exposure. Suppose there is an X factor in the liver that makes it less efficient when it has to metabolize large quantities of alcohol. If large quantities are never introduced, this vulnerability has no meaning. This is simply one illustration of the response to alcohol; for a problem to arise, there must be a genetic vulnerability as well as an amount of alcohol consumption great enough to expose it.

Researchers are now speculating that some people are born with alternate metabolic pathways for substances like alcohol—pathways that only come into use when the normal routes are overtaxed. Those who have such pathways would be much more capable of handling the effects of alcohol or substances that compete with it, such as Valium.

Researchers are also speculating that people metabolize differently at different hours. "I think we don't give enough attention to the fact that for some people there are noticeable differences for how much alcohol they can consume under certain circumstances," Professor Straus observes. "There are people who cross several time zones during the day, and often experience different responses to medication, or to substances like alcohol, depending on the time zone they're in. There is a whole variety of our body functions that tend to vary within the twenty-four-hour cycle."

Straus cites himself as an example. He can easily handle a beer with his dinner, but a beer at lunch puts him to sleep. He knows he's more sensitive to alcohol at that hour, but he doesn't know why. He cites a number of studies in which women report an increased sensitivity to alcohol just prior to menstruation.

Aging is yet another example of how the body's response to alcohol changes. Few people can drink as much in their later years as they did when they were younger. The body just can't handle it. The storage time of the alcohol is greater, and its elimination slower, so the "bioavailability" of the drug is increased. In practical terms, this means that it takes less alcohol to produce the same effect.

For all these reasons, then, what is safe for one drinker may not be safe for another—and that is why there is no magic safe-drinking number that can be applied uniformly to each and every drinker. The answer will vary depending on one's sex, physical characteristics, genetic predisposition and family history. (If others in your family have had physical problems with alcohol, there does seem to be at least a statistical predisposition for the problems to pass through you.)

Constructing a personal balance sheet is made all the more complex by one tantalizing contradiction—that alcohol, fatal in large doses, may actually improve health and extend life when taken in small amounts.

5 · Is Moderate Drinking Beneficial?

That human beings have drunk throughout history in spite
of the problems associated with drinking and the restrictions placed upon it says something about alcohol's com-
pelling qualities. They are many, not the least of which is
that if some individuals were not tranquilized by a drink
at day's end, they might not live long enough to die of
cirrhosis or cancer.

Both psychological and physiological components are
involved in alcohol's beneficence. Let us consider them in
that order.

Mark Keller of the Center of Alcohol Studies at Rutgers
University has imagined what it must have been like on that
day when one of our prehistoric forebears, returning from
an unsuccessful hunt, happened upon a mishmash of fruit
fermenting in a primitive vessel or the hollow of a rock.
"It not only satisfied his hunger and thirst but also made
him feel exceptionally good all over; less tired; less achy;
and even less disappointed. Maybe even more: maybe he
saw wondrous visions and felt full of divine courage and
demonic derring-do; he could talk back to his carping wife
and he uttered words which, although not understandable,
sounded inspired and portentous."

Through the millennia, it has been alcohol's capacity to facilitate just such "attitude adjustment," as one user describes it, that has made it so popular and provoked such enormous impact. Injudicious use has created sorrow beyond measure, as well as uncounted expense, but the moderate use of alcohol has established it, beyond recall, as the oil of social intercourse. Nowhere is that fact of life more in evidence than in America in the 1980s.

No one has come up with a precise figure, but various consumption studies indicate that the cocktail hour could now be an established ritual in as many as 20 million American homes. While the country has never been a "pub culture" like England and Scotland, the "happy hour" and singles bars—unknown a quarter of a century ago—have become as much a part of the social ritual for young Americans as watching football on television. Most authorities consider the use of alcohol in such settings as a beneficial rite when practiced in moderation, a simple and safe transition from workaday worries to pleasant evenings.

In the process of producing this valuable psychological service, moderate amounts of alcohol appear to contribute to "wellness" in a variety of ways. Since stress is often a component of disease, particularly heart disease and cancer, many doctors believe that a drink or two in the evening is good preventive medicine. Authorities have long suspected that many neurotics and even potential psychotics manage to keep themselves out of hospitals and institutions by self-medicating with alcohol. Geriatric homes note a cut in the amount of medication they dispense once wine is served regularly with dinner. Patients comment on the salubrious effect of alcohol as an aid to social functioning—an innocuous statement unless you understand the killing effect of loneliness among the elderly.

In the late 1960s, studies were made in the Boston area as to what impact, if any, the introduction of small amounts of alcohol into the daily diets of elderly men would have on their behavior. At the outset of one study, twenty-six of the patients in a ward for senile men were incontinent, and the same number needed safety restraints. Then the institution began to serve beer with cheese and crackers in the afternoon. Two months later the number of incontinent men had fallen to nine, and only four required safety restraints. The number of ambulatory patients rose from seven to twenty-five, and the number willing to participate in group activities tripled. When the study began, three quarters of the patients were being medicated with Thorazine, a psychotropic drug; a month after alcoholic beverages were introduced, the use of Thorazine had been eliminated.

Was it the beer these men received or the tender loving care that accompanied it that accounted for their change in behavior? Is it the alcohol in the cocktail we drink at day's end or the fellowship that surrounds it that causes us to forget our cares?

The popular assumption has always been that the effects of alcohol are a consequence of its pharmacological properties. Without question, that is true to an extent. We know that alcohol, the substance, packs a wallop if only because of its deleterious effect on motor performance, coordination and reaction time. But the social response to alcohol is another matter altogether. At the doses most social drinkers consume, the physiological reaction is at best undefined. What gives it definition are the perceptions we bring to the drinking event, and the event itself.

Few social scientists in the alcohol-research field would dispute the importance of the drinker's "givens" as a determinant of his response to alcohol, but they would argue that the environment and its expectations of the drinker have probably shaped those "givens" to a great extent. Many social scientists believe that the manner in which drinkers behave when drinking has at least as much to do with society's expectations of them as it does with the drinkers' chemical response to alcohol. Craig MacAndrew and Robert Edgerton have shown, for example, that drinkers in different cultures react in completely different ways when they're drunk, and almost invariably in accord with what their cultures expect of drunks. Our expectation is that a sufficient amount of alcohol will produce sexual arousal and physical aggressiveness, and that's what often happens. In some cultures the expectation is that people who drink too much will go to sleep—and they do.

In our culture, alcohol has been used as a kind of social excuse. If a person has been drinking and others see that he has, then he can be more or less let off the hook for some kinds of conduct that in a sober person would be dealt with much more harshly. It's the expectation of such sanctions, some psychologists and sociologists say, that not only encourages many persons to drink but actually precipitates their aggressive, often antisocial conduct. "Just because alcohol affects motor behavior, we have generalized to assume that it also affects social behavior," one psychologist observes. "There's nothing in the literature that says there's something about alcohol, the drug, that makes you act in an immoral fashion."

Today some exciting new experiments appear to validate the role of expectation in alcohol's effects. "We now have the first solid evidence that psychological processes have as much—or more—to do with some drinking behaviors than do the physical effects of alcohol," psychologist G. Alan Marlatt of the University of Washington, and Damaris J. Rohsenow, an assistant professor at the University of Wisconsin, reported.* "In a series of experiments with a unique 'balanced placebo' design, psychologists have shown that people will act in certain stereotypical ways when they drink, even if they are drinking tonic water but have been told they are drinking vodka and tonic."

* *Psychology Today* (December 1981).

Drinking comportment, those studies appear to show, "influence our reactions to alcohol in ways we have previously failed to acknowledge," the authors wrote. Among those reactions:

- Men who are told that they are drinking alcohol become less anxious in social situations, even when they've been drinking a nonalcoholic placebo.
- Alcoholics, supposedly triggered by a physiologically based addictive mechanism after only one or two drinks, have precisely the same craving after one or two placebo drinks. More surprising yet, they develop no craving after consuming alcoholic drinks they've been told are placebos.
- Men who believe they are drinking vodka but are actually drinking tonic water become more aggressive; when the circumstances are reversed—when they *are* drinking vodka but think it's simply tonic water, they do not become more aggressive.
- The same flip-flop effect appears in regard to drinking and sexual conduct. Men who think they're drinking alcohol become sexually aroused even when drinking placebos. Women, too, report increased feelings of arousal after drinking what they've been told are alcoholic beverages, but tests of their vaginal blood flow indicate that they are physiologically less aroused.

"Because of our exposure to drinking models presented both in real life and in the media, we have come to expect that people will sometimes do things under the influence of alcohol that they would never do otherwise," the authors wrote. "Alcohol is frequently consumed in relaxed, convivial settings in which sexual advances, for example, are appropriate. In this sense, alcohol acts as a cue for sexual behavior. The cue effects are the same regardless of the pharmacological properties of alcohol, as long as the people involved believe they are really drinking liquor."

In one of their experiments with alcoholic subjects, the volunteers were required to go without a drink for eight hours prior to appearing. No honor system was involved; all of the subjects were required to show a zero reading on a breath analysis test. A number of the subjects, as a consequence, arrived with the shakes. After the drinking session, one of the men who had expected to receive alcohol but had actually received tonic water began to act as though he was intoxicated. He stumbled around the room, and tried to make a date with a female member of the research team.

Numbers of other experiences have since borne out the results of the experiments, according to Marlatt. In one instance, he had been counseling a man who insisted that he needed several beers every day in order to relax, but who at the same time was worried about his intake. One day the psychologist proposed that they visit BARLAB, a classroom at the University of Washington that has been converted into a small cocktail lounge, complete with dim lights and soft music, for the purpose of conducting research experiments. "Let's have a few drinks," Marlatt said, "and you'll tell me what it feels like as you drink." His patient instantly agreed.

When they got to BARLAB, Marlatt went behind the bar and poured him a "beer," carefully keeping the can out of sight. Halfway through his second beer, the patient exclaimed, "There! I can feel it starting to hit!"

"Exactly what are you feeling?" Marlatt asked.

"I feel a warm glow spreading through my body. That's it! That's the feeling! It usually starts halfway through my second beer."

"The beer you've been drinking doesn't have any alcohol in it," Marlatt told him then.

The man refused to believe him, until Marlatt went behind the bar and produced a can of near-beer. The man shook his head in disbelief. "You mean I'm making myself relax?" he asked at last.

"That looks like a big part of it," the psychologist said.

Whatever the cause—be it situational or pharmacological —alcohol does make most people euphoric when drunk in moderation. That's what makes it so attractive. "People drink in order to attempt to cope with what's going on in life," Marlatt observes. "It's a balance of 'wants' and 'shoulds.' Where people exist in patterns where there are a lot of 'shoulds,' a lot of tensions build up, and there's a lot of heavy drinking at the end of the day. The drinks are perceived as 'wants'—something for themselves."

If drinking to forget is the objective, that may happen to a point because more recent experiences tend to be put aside and even momentarily forgotten with the first dose of alcohol. But after a certain amount has been drunk by a person attempting to drown his sorrows, the exercise becomes self-defeating because alcohol in sufficient quantity tends to reinforce the mood the drinker brings to it. That is an excellent illustration of alcohol's double-barreled effect.

Many people believe that alcohol is a stimulant. Others consider it a depressant. In fact, it is both, but not at the same time. In low doses it acts as an "upper," not only as a social lubricant that rids one of tensions but also as a facilitator of motor response. Some persons are more skillful after consuming small quantities of alcohol, the probable reason being that relaxed muscles contribute to smoother performance, and a relaxed performer doesn't try so hard that he ties himself in knots.

In very moderate doses alcohol can actually increase one's ability to solve problems, probably because it creates a sense of self-confidence, well-being and hopefulness. Numbers of studies of male social drinkers have shown a corollary between the consumption of alcohol and perceptions of power. "Social power" fantasies—those in which power would be exercised in behalf of a group or a cause—appear after two or three drinks. "Personal power" fantasies—in which power would be used to advance one's own interests—appear after intakes of larger amounts. "Men drink primarily to feel stronger," D. C. McClelland and his co-authors concluded in *The Drinking Man*.* "Those for whom personalized power is a particular concern drink more heavily." Says Marlatt: "If the drinker experiences a loss of personal control in a stressful situation and has no other adequate coping response available, the probability of drinking will increase. Alcohol consumption, under these conditions, serves to restore the person's sense of personal control because of its enhancing effects on arousal and thoughts of personal power or control."

Moderate amounts of alcohol can also enhance the appreciation of sex, and may even contribute to performance. Perception is heightened, arguments are avoided and the appetite is enhanced. Small doses can also make for sounder sleep.

But as more and more alcohol is consumed, it does become a depressant that inhibits and retards performance. The drinker becomes sleepy, his speech slurs and his coordination is impaired. If he drinks enough, he will become unconscious, and a large enough dose can kill him.

One of the prevalent myths about alcohol is that it will warm the body against the ravages of cold weather; St. Bernard dogs with small casks tied to their collars are staples of cartoons involving persons marooned in the snow. But using alcohol to warm the body in such conditions can actually prove fatal because the alcohol can drop the body's temperature still further. Alcohol lowers the body's thermo-

* New York: Free Press, 1972.

stat, a small cluster of cells in the hypothalamus at the center of the brain.

Under normal conditions, however, alcohol does provide energy, approximately seven calories per gram, a modest amount of which can be utilized in the performance of work. Alcohol also provides nutrition. To the extent that yeasts are present in a beverage, the drinker of that beverage is fortifying himself with protein and B complex vitamins.

But these are almost fringe benefits compared to a theory under investigation that has inspired great excitement and attention.

The most impressive benefit consigned to alcohol is the possibility that it might actually extend life if taken in small doses on a fairly regular basis. That possibility was first given substance during Prohibition by Raymond Pearl of the Institute for Biological Research at the Johns Hopkins University in Baltimore and caused a tremendous controversy at the time it was published almost sixty years ago. Pearl's classic study, *Alcohol and Longevity*,* detailed experiments with fowls that had led him to question the widespread belief in those days that small amounts of alcohol could be lethal. Those fowls exposed to daily doses of alcohol vapors lived longer than those that got nothing but plain food and water.

"While the experimental results . . . on longevity clearly cannot be transferred directly to man because of the different modes of intake of the alcohol," Pearl wrote, "nevertheless they are not without indirect value in the discussion of the human problem. They indicate, so far as they go, that there is no inherently necessary, biologically deleterious effect of ethyl alcohol in moderate doses upon duration of

* New York: Knopf, 1926.

life, however long continued and frequently taken, provided it is administered in a manner which is not immediately and directly harmful physiologically. Or, put in the other way about, the *experimental results prove that ethyl alcohol can be so administered to some living organisms as not to affect harmfully the duration of life.*"

The italics Pearl gave to that passage undoubtedly reflected his awareness of the controversial nature of his statement.

Pearl went on to study a large and homogeneous sample of the working population of Baltimore. He found that moderate drinkers not only did not appear to shorten their lives by drinking, they exhibited lower mortality rates than abstainers. "This superiority is not great in the male moderate drinkers, and may not be significant statistically," he said, "but it certainly gives no support to the almost universal belief that alcohol always shortens life, even in moderate quantities."

Many research studies since have replicated Pearl's findings in one form or another. One, known as the Honolulu Heart Study, sought to establish the relationship, if any, of both alcohol and coffee to coronary heart disease. The investigators, led by Katushiko Yano, worked with 7,705 Japanese men between forty-five and sixty-eight years of age at the outset of the study. First the participants received a complete physical checkup. Six years later, 287 of them had developed coronary heart disease. The highest proportion of heart attacks had been suffered by ex-drinkers. Teetotalers were second. Drinkers had the fewest heart attacks. The type of alcoholic beverage they drank did not seem to matter; no matter what it was, drinkers fared better than nondrinkers. (Beer was the most popular beverage, and beer drinkers, proportionately, had the fewest heart attacks of all.) Nondrinkers also died in greater numbers from other types heart disease than drinkers, and light drinkers—those who drank half an ounce of absolute alcohol a day—suffered more heart attacks than those who drank 2 ounces of absolute alcohol a day.

Another benchmark study, in Framingham, Massachusetts, used monthly consumption to arrive at mortality comparisons. The subjects were men and women of all ages. Abstainers and heavy drinkers had the highest mortality rates, moderate drinkers the lowest. The same result was recently confirmed in a ten-year study of civil servants in London. More than 1,400 men initially aged forty to sixty-four reported their alcohol intake during selected three-day periods. Cardiovascular mortality was most common among nondrinkers, and noncardiovascular mortality most common among heavy drinkers. The relationship between drinking and mortality was independent of smoking, blood pressure, plasma cholesterol and grade of employment.

The most convincing corollary between moderate drinking and longevity to date has emerged from a long-range study at the Kaiser-Permanente Medical Center in Oakland, California. Between July 1964 and August 1968, some 88,000 group members had undergone multiphasic health examinations; in 1970, epidemiologist Gary D. Friedman decided that the accumulation of such an extraordinary human data base represented a rare opportunity to search for previously undetected predictors of heart attack. In the past, other studies had identified certain risk factors such as high blood pressure, high cholesterol levels, diabetes and smoking. But Friedman and his associates on the Kaiser-Permanente staff reasoned that other risk factors probably existed and needed to be unearthed. A fishing expedition seemed in order, and for an epidemiologist it was the equivalent of a lone angler stumbling onto a heavily stocked stream at the start of the season. What Friedman and colleagues had going for them was not only the data of nearly 88,000 checkups but the knowledge that the patients would be followed for a number of years. The information collected at the time of the checkups could thus be correlated to heart attacks that might occur subsequent to the checkups.

The study established an inverse statistical relationship between moderate alcohol use and the prospect of heart attacks. The same finding had been hinted at in the Framingham Study, but not much had been made of it, either because the data base wasn't large enough to give the researchers courage to be conclusive or else because the statistical relationship didn't seem quite so striking. The Oakland study had no such problems; it had perhaps the biggest data base any researchers had ever worked with in the field of alcohol research, and its major finding was unmistakable: nondrinkers were 30 percent more likely to have heart attacks than drinkers.

The Oakland study had been carefully controlled for all the other factors generally associated with heart attacks. Whatever findings emerged could be considered to be independent of these other factors. Moreover, the 30 precent figure was a comparison between nondrinkers and drinkers of any amount; *all* drinkers enjoyed a statistical edge over abstainers when it came to the prospect of heart attacks.

Since that time, the Kaiser-Permanente group has done three separate analyses that confirm the inverse relationship between drinking and heart attacks. Nondrinkers consistently suffer more heart attacks than drinkers.

Arthur L. Klatsky, chief of cardiology at Kaiser-Permanente, is impressed. With four separate studies to back him up, he says, "If a person took two drinks metronomically day after day from adulthood on, he would be substantially less likely to have coronary heart trouble than if he didn't. If we could do lifetime experiments on people, if we could control what they did, taking a group of people at age twenty and saying, 'Now, for forty years, we're going to control your alcohol intake and your smoking and your exercise and all of the other things associated with coronary disease,' and if we could see to it that these people took two glasses of wine or two beers or even two shots of whiskey every day, I suspect it would turn out that they would end up having less coronary disease."

Why? What is it about drinking that seems to protect the heart? One possible answer is that there are certain physiological and biochemical consequences to the consumption of alcohol that could make the circulation system more efficient. For years the most popular explanation of this possibility was that alcohol acts as a "vasodilator," relaxing the body's blood vessels and making the work of the heart that much easier as it pumps blood through the body. But in recent years that theory has come under question, to be replaced by another, which scientists consider much more promising. Alcohol, they say, seems to elevate the body's levels of high-density lipoprotein (HDL) cholesterol, the so-called good cholesterol, the same desirable effect one gets from exercise. This blood protein protects against heart disease by acting as a scavenger, carrying off unwanted particles from the blood vessels— a "Drano" of the human system. The effect of this action is to permit the blood to flow more freely through the arteries and thereby make the heart's work easier.

An experiment by Dr. Joseph Barboriak of Milwaukee and his colleagues in the mid-1970s appeared to reinforce the idea that something about alcohol acts to unclog the arteries. Twenty-five hundred patients at two Milwaukee hospitals who were undergoing diagnostic coronary arteriography because of various heart-related ailments volunteered to participate in the study. The results clearly established an inverse relationship between coronary artery occlusion and the amount of alcohol consumed—meaning that the more the subjects used alcohol, the less blockage there was in their arteries. To the researchers, the results supported the association between alcohol and increased levels of HDL.

Numbers of studies in recent years have related the

moderate consumption of alcohol to the production of HDL. One of the most emphatic was a study of nearly 10,000 persons in the United States and Canada conducted under the auspices of the National Heart, Lung and Blood Institute in Bethesda, Maryland. The participants in the study represented a wide cross section of people who reported to ten different lipid-research clinics scattered through North America. Previous studies, notably the Framingham Study, had ascertained that persons with high HDL levels were less likely to suffer heart attacks than those with low HDL levels. The institute's study, the first to look at how life styles affect HDL, confirmed the relationship of moderate drinking to high levels of the "good cholesterol." (The "bad cholesterol" is carried by low-density lipoprotein, or LDL. High levels of LDL increase the risk of coronary disease.)

A study performed in San Francisco by Dr. Stephen B. Hulley and Sara Gordon adds further proof to the alcohol and HDL connection. They found that the HDL levels of social drinkers were higher than those of teetotalers by as much as 33 percent. And when the social drinkers abstained from drinking for two weeks, their HDL levels dropped by 15 percent.

From whatever source the benefits derive, the evidence would seem to suggest that drinking moderately enhances one's chance of extending life, particularly as compared to heavy drinkers or abstainers. That proposition was the focus of a paper by Dr. Thomas Turner of Johns Hopkins and two of his colleagues which not only endorsed the premise but rewrote the definition of moderate drinking.* Where most monitors of alcohol and health have tended to follow "Anstie's limit,"† the authors of the 1981 paper

---

* "The Beneficial Side of Moderate Alcohol Use," *Johns Hopkins Medical Journal* (February 1981).
† Named after a nineteenth-century English physician who determined that 1.5 ounces of absolute alcohol a day—the equivalent of three contemporary American drinks—was a safe limit.

argued that "expanded knowledge of alcohol metabolism and documented intake-effect relationship indicated that adults can safely exceed this daily amount." Said Turner, Virginia Lee Bennett and Hector Hernandez: "Chronic ill effects in man are rare below a daily intake of 80 grams (approximately six drinks) and thus permit upper limits of moderate drinking to be established on a more rational basis."

That "rational basis" was a formula, based on body weight, setting forth "upper limits of allowable daily alcohol consumption" that would permit a 154-pound person to drink 6 ounces of 80-proof spirits or 20 ounces of 12% table wine or 53 ounces of 3.6% beer a day and still be considered a moderate drinker. A 220-pound man could drink as much as 8.6 ounces of spirits or 29 ounces of wine or 76 ounces of beer with the assurance that he would do himself no harm.*

"In general," the authors concluded, "ill effects from moderate alcohol use have not been documented, if escalation of intake is avoided. Possible exceptions, for which adequate documentation is currently lacking, are effects on driving by youths and young adults, and on the fetus."

For Dr. Turner, who recently turned eighty, that study and its recommendations fulfilled a commitment made dur-

---

* The formula: Intake should not exceed .8 gram per kilogram on any day, with an absolute limit of 80 grams and no more than an average of 7 grams per kilogram per day over any three-day period.

A simplified formula, subsequently devised, provides each individual with precise amounts he or she can safely drink under the Turner, et al., guidelines.
   • To determine the number of ounces of 80-proof spirits allowable in any twenty-four-hour period, divide your weight in pounds by 30. Example: 150 pounds divided by 30 = 5 ounces of 80-proof spirits.
   • To determine the number of ounces of 12% wine allowable in any twenty-four-hour period, divide your weight in pounds by 9. Example: 150 pounds divided by 9 = 16.6 ounces of 12% wine.
   • To determine the number of ounces of 4.5% beer allowable in any twenty-four-hour period, divide your weight in pounds by 3. Example: 150 pounds divided by 3 = 50 ounces of beer.

ing Prohibition and intensified when he joined the Johns Hopkins medical faculty in 1927 and came under the influence of Raymond Pearl, the author of *Alcohol and Longevity*. When Turner retired forty years later, he was asked by the university to chair a committee to coordinate alcohol research. Subsequently he became the chairman of a small medical advisory committee of the United States Brewers Association, composed of men who had distinguished themselves in other fields of medicine and research but were without a special knowledge of alcohol. The hope, Turner recalls, was that such men would be able to take a more "objective look" at the type of research under way in the alcohol field than he believed it was being given.

"What I'm looking at are the ninety percent of drinkers who drink sensibly," Turner explained during a conversation in 1982. "I think they deserve some guidance as to what is reasonable and sensible on the average. This doesn't mean that every person should stick to this formula. It doesn't mean that everyone should aspire to drink up to those limits every day. Far from it. But there's been a great reluctance on the part of everyone in a knowledgeable position to say that it might be all right to drink up to certain limits. In a way, this is my main contribution. Everyone talks in average amounts, average persons. This isn't the way it works. It seems to me that every individual should have a formula to guide him that applies to him and him alone.

"You take the reported data of people who are in trouble with alcohol, and all of them virtually without exception have been and are drinking a lot of alcohol. What we did was to say that most of these people are drinking at least a hundred grams a day [seven-plus drinks], and some, a relatively small proportion, eighty grams [just under six drinks] and then we built a safety factor into that." From this reasoning—based, Turner emphasizes, not on original research but on a "critical review of the literature"—the weight-related formula emerged.

With such a formula, as well as all of the foregoing, to back him up, the social drinker would have good reason to believe that his drinking latitude was wider than he had ever dared imagine, and that drinking at these generous rates would probably do him some good.

But such conclusions might be premature. As suggestive as the evidence in behalf of moderate drinking's salutary effects may seem, numbers of questions must be answered before even those engaged in the research can say positively that alcohol, itself, makes the difference.

Are moderate drinkers protected by increased high-density lipoprotein levels and other benefits of alcohol—the management of stress, for example—or are they simply the kind of people relaxed enough about life to enjoy a drink in the evening? Alcoholics and abstainers are remarkably similar in certain respects—uptight, easily stressed, rigid—that can put a mortal strain on life. It may be that people who are willing to take a drink are simply less tense than abstainers and, as psychologist Richard Jessor of the University of Colorado has noted, living a kind of life style that helps to fend off problems. Some researchers suspect it's not the alcohol but the moderate drinkers' more relaxed approach that enables them to live longer. Says Dr. Louis J. West, director of the Neuropsychiatric Institute at UCLA: "It might be the attitude that will cause the person to relax and have a drink rather than being a stiff-necked, hard-driving, teetotaling personality who might push himself into a cardiac model."

Moderate drinkers, in short, may enjoy living more than abstainers do, and as a consequence live longer. Or it may be that what transpires with moderate drinkers is a further illustration of the wisdom of *ne quid nimis*—moderation in all things—counseled more than two thousand years ago by Andria, the lady of Andros.

That was the burden of a benchmark study of life-enhancing habits conducted among 7,000 California residents from 1965 to 1974 by the Human Population Laboratory of the California State Department of Public Health. The study concluded that people who have moderate and regular life styes, including moderate use of alcohol, have a better chance to live longer—men by as much as eleven years and women by seven—than those who don't.

One of the problems in attempting to discover the effect of drinking on health is that drinking is always associated with other habits, some of which may have as great a bearing on health as the consumption of alcohol.

"Drinking is also part of a larger social context," Nancy Day, a social epidemiologist, observes. "When viewed in this manner, drinking becomes one of many variables, all of which are interrelated. This is an important issue when we look at mortality and drinking, since many of the variables that correlate with a particular drinking behavior are themselves strongly correlated with mortality. We know, for example, that a heavy drinker is more likely to be a cigarette smoker, lower class, and male. Each of these factors is in itself an important predictor of mortality. What we need to do is separate these various effects to determine the relationship between alcohol use and mortality."

It was Nancy Day who applied these basic research principles to the question of whether moderate drinking is truly as beneficial as the mortality studies seem to indicate it is, and who came up with an answer that gave many of her colleagues pause.

Who were the abstainers who had died prematurely? Day wondered. Were they "pure" abstainers—persons who had never had a drink? Or were they former drinkers who were no longer drinking for reasons of health? If the latter were predominant, or even significant, then their poor health might account for the higher death rates among abstainers. Various studies had sought to confront these questions, but none had really resolved them. Day, then a doctoral candidate at the University of California, Berkeley, set about to answer the questions with a heroic-sized piece of research. First she pooled all of the data obtained by Berkeley's Alcohol Research Group from 1962 through 1974 in almost 5,000 interviews. Then she identified which of the interview subjects had died in the interval between 1962 and the late 1970s. Finally she obtained death-certificate data that could enable her to establish the cause of death, and then correlated this data to the drinking patterns described in the initial interviews. These were her findings:

- Those who drank the greatest amounts each time they drank had the highest mortality rates.
- Those who drank infrequently or in moderate amounts when they did drink—less than two drinks—had the lowest mortality rates.
- Those who didn't drink at all had a much lower mortality rate than the heavy drinkers but a much higher mortality rate than those who drank lightly.

Up to this point Day's findings correlated with the previous studies at Framingham, in Honolulu and in Oakland. But then Day did something the others hadn't done. She broke down the abstainers into two categories—those who had never taken a drink in their lives, and those who used to drink unspecified amounts. The results were startling:

- Pure abstainers had death rates as low as the moderate drinkers.
- Former drinkers who had become abstainers accounted for most of the abstainers' excess deaths.

The assumption is that the former drinkers became abstainers for reasons of health, and that it was their drinking that had made them ill. If the assumption is valid, the reason abstainers appear to compare so poorly to moderate drinkers in mortality tables is because unhealthy former drinkers are loading the category. According to this finding, abstinence per se is *not* less healthful than moderate drinking.

As far as is known, Day's study is the first to "pull apart" the rise in mortality at the bottom of alcohol-consumption statistics. While her findings would need to be replicated, they do appear to cast doubts on the relationship of moderate drinking to longevity. Said Don Cahalan in an article in the journal of the American Heart Association:* "These findings would incline one to be cautious about concluding that small amounts of alcohol taken frequently tend to stave off heart attacks."

That, as we'll see next, is far from the only caution being expressed today about social drinking.

* *Circulation* (September 1981).

6 · The Case for Caution I

Cirrhosis, Cancer and Hypertension

Several years ago, researchers at the Kaiser-Permanente Medical Center in Oakland, California, determined to use the center's extraordinary data base to see whether they might answer the most important question associated with the consumption of alcohol, to wit: At what point does drinking become a threat to life?

Out of the nearly 88,000 members of the health plan who had had medical examinations between July 1964 and August 1968, the researchers chose four groups of 2,015 persons each, well matched for age, sex, race and cigarette smoking. The groups were divided into 1) nondrinkers, 2) those who drank two drinks a day or less, 3) those who drank three to five drinks a day, and 4) those who drank six or more drinks a day. In 1978, ten years after the members' last examination, the researchers pored over the California death indexes for the names of 3,190 of the 8,060 original subjects who had been dropped from the health group's rolls, a method of mortality surveillance estimated to be between 82 and 92 percent accurate. The survey turned up 745 of the original group who had died in the interval. Here is how it broke down in terms of the drinking groups:

1) Nondrinkers: 177
2) Two drinks or less: 126
3) Three to five drinks: 187
4) Six or more drinks: 255

Those who drank three to five drinks a day had a mortality rate almost 50 percent higher than those who drank two drinks or less a day. The mortality rate of abstainers was only fractionally lower than that of the three-to-five-drinks-a-day group. The heaviest drinkers had a doubled mortality rate, compared to those who drank two drinks a day or less.

Writing in the *Annals of Internal Medicine*, in August 1981, Arthur Klatsky, Gary Friedman and Abraham B. Siegelaub summed up: "The data presented here indicate that the threshold for increased mortality risk lies in the range of regular use of three to five drinks daily and that the risk rises sharply at six or more drinks per day."

In the past, the risk of early death due to drinking had been widely perceived as beginning at elevated levels of consumption—at least six drinks a day. Here, now, was a major piece of research indicating that the threshold of risk was located at a much lower level of consumption, one identified almost universally today as "social drinking."

Because the study could not account for every factor that might contribute to premature death, it could not be said conclusively that the use of alcohol in increasing amounts was the critical factor. But an analysis of the causes of deaths indicated that it could have been; most of the untimely deaths, the researchers found, were associated with drinking—accidents, suicides, homicides *and* diseases.

Violent death associated with alcohol—the so-called acute, or intoxicating, effects—is an old and familiar story.

But the possibility that there might be long-term or chronic effects on health, most of them invisible for many years, even for persons who regard themselves, and are regarded by others, as social drinkers, has arisen only in recent years.

The drinks-to-death ratio in the Kaiser-Permanente study had actually been anticipated by an earlier study in the Bay Area, the one conducted by the Human Population Laboratory of the California State Department of Health. An analysis of the life styles of some 7,000 deceased persons in Alameda County showed that those who had been drinking three or more drinks on each occasion had higher death rates than those who had been drinking one or two.

Taken by themselves, such studies are insufficient to incriminate heavy social drinking. What gives them added credence is that they appear to tie in with a number of other recent studies on the relationship of alcohol consumption to specific diseases that make the same disquieting connection.

To understand what follows, it will be helpful to familiarize ourselves with the standard most commonly employed by researchers in distinguishing levels of drinking: how many grams of absolute alcohol a person consumes each day.*

---

* Here is a formula for determining how many grams of absolute alcohol are in a drink. It looks hard, but it isn't.

Step One: $(A \times B) \ (29.57353) = C$
Step Two: $(C) \ (.789) = D$

A = % of alcohol (if expressed as proof, divide by 2)
B = fluid ounces of beverage
C = milliliters of absolute alcohol
D = grams of absolute alcohol

Suppose you want to find out how many grams of absolute alcohol are in a 1.5-ounce dry martini made with 80-proof gin.

A = .80 divided by 2 = .40
B = 1.5 ounces

First step: Multiply $.40 \times 1.5 \times 29.57353$ (the number of milliliters in a fluid ounce). The result is 17.74 milliliters of absolute alcohol.

Second step: To convert to grams, multiply $17.74 \times .789$.

Result: The number of grams of absolute alcohol in a 1.5-ounce dry martini is 14.

While the standard has varied through the years, in general researchers today accept a "drink" as being equal to 14 grams of absolute alcohol. That is the approximate number of grams that would be in 1.5 fluid ounces of 80-proof spirits, 3 fluid ounces of port or cream sherry containing 20 percent alcohol, or 5 fluid ounces of 12% table wine. (Twelve ounces of 4.5% beer is 12.6 grams.)

The medical problem most commonly associated with excessive drinking is cirrhosis of the liver, which eventually destroys that organ's ability to function. Life can't continue without the liver; when it goes, so do we.

Alcohol produces an immediate effect on the liver that is actually visible under a microscope. A single dry martini substantially increases the fat in the liver, and a sufficient amount of alcohol over the years can produce a condition known as "fatty liver." There is some disagreement as to whether fatty liver is or isn't a precursor of cirrhosis, but none whatever as to its implications. It's a telltale sign of excessive drinking, and if permitted to develop sufficiently, can impede liver function all on its own. The cells of the liver fill with triglyceride droplets, which are the major fat in blood and interfere with normal biochemical and metabolic functions of the cells.

Fatty liver often results from bouts of heavy drinking lasting several weeks. One California internist estimates that half the new patients he examines, most of them in their twenties and early thirties, have the beginning indications of fatty liver—a condition that quickly disappears, in most cases, if drinking is stopped.

Alcoholic hepatitis, which most researchers deem a precursor of cirrhosis, is also caused by heavy consumption, but unlike fatty liver, is not so easily reversible. Between 10 and 30 percent of all those contracting alcoholic hepatitis die of the disease.

But it's cirrhosis that habitual drinkers most fear.

"Along comes that thousandth literary lunch and pow! The dreaded wrecking ball of cirrhosis is unslung," as Richard Selzer, a physician and author, put it. "The roofs and walls of the hallways, complaining under their burden of excess fat, groan and buckle. Inflammation sets in, and whole roomsful of liver cells implode and die. And in their place comes the scarring that twists and distorts the channels, pulling them into impossible angulations."*

As the liver becomes scarred, the small bile ducts become plugged. The bile, unable to flow through its normal channels any longer, backs up into the bloodstream. Havoc results. The skin yellows, the eyes become rheumy. The belly swells. The face and neck become spidered with blood vessels. Within the liver, the pressure builds; when the pressure exceeds the tolerance, the inflow of the blood into the liver is impeded by the swelling. That causes pressure on the small blood vessels. When these veins become swollen enough, they start to hemorrhage. Then they rupture, which produces painful and dangerous internal hemorrhage. When the poisons in the body reach a certain level, the mind begins to fail. Eventually, death results.

Cirrhosis accounts for some 30,000 deaths a year in the United States, with native Americans and blacks showing much higher percentages than whites relative to their populations. The cirrhosis mortality rate of black Americans is almost twice that of white Americans, a phenomenon that researchers are at a loss to explain. In 1950 the cirrhosis rate for blacks was slightly lower than it was for whites. By 1967 the rate for blacks had more than tripled, while the rate for whites was increasing at a less startling pace.

Women, generally, appear to be much more vulnerable than men to liver problems associated with alcohol con-

* *Esquire* (April 1974).

sumption, and with cirrhosis in particular. (At present, fewer women than men develop cirrhosis because fewer women drink.) Alcoholic women develop cirrhosis at lower levels of consumption and after shorter bouts of excessive drinking than do alcoholic men; and twice as many alcoholic women as alcoholic men develop the disease. (Women in their forties and fifties are particularly susceptible, possibly because of hormonal changes.) But the susceptibility extends to nonalcoholic women as well.

Not all chronic drinkers develop cirrhosis, and not all cases of cirrhosis are caused by drinking. Estimates of the contribution of alcohol to cirrhosis range widely, between 22 and 95 percent, with most of the estimates clustered between 60 and 80 percent.

Whether there is any relationship at all of alcohol to diseases of the liver still ranks in some minds as a "dubious and unsubstantiated" myth, to use the words of a skeptic writing in the *Atlantic* in December 1979. The argument, focused largely on cirrhosis, seems to rest on two ideas. The first is that people who don't drink also develop cirrhosis, young people and prisoners of war being two examples. The second deals with diet. One of the cardinal assumptions in the alcohol field until recent years was that cirrhosis was a consequence not of the substance itself but of the propensity of heavy drinkers to eat sparingly and sporadically. Even today, the theory retains its adherents, and they are backed up principally by the research of Dr. Arthur J. Patek of Boston. Patek, a self-described "nut" on the relationship of nutrition to the long-term effects of alcohol, believes that the nutritional state of the drinker determines to a great extent what will be the biomedical consequences of his drinking. Regular, well-balanced meals, he feels, can set up a "nutritional defense" against alcohol. In one study of 304 alcoholics he found that the non-cirrhotic patients had consumed more food calories and more protein during the two years prior to their hospitalization than the cirrhotic patients had. In a much earlier experiment at Columbia University he had been able to achieve significant improvement in more than 100 cirrhotic patients by putting them on a nutritious diet full of protein and vitamin B concentrates. Whether abstinence from alcohol, bed rest, diuretics and supportive care also contributed to the improvement is a matter of conjecture; whatever the reason, the patients receiving the nutritious diet showed marked physical improvement. At the end of one year, 65 percent of the treated patients were still alive, compared to 39 percent of the controls, cirrhotics who were not receiving the same treatment; at the end of the second year, 50 percent of the treated patients were still alive, compared to 21 percent of the controls; and at the end of five years, 30 percent of the treated patients were still alive, compared to only 7 percent of the controls.

"The mechanism by which alcohol excess leads to cirrhosis is not fully understood," Dr. Patek noted. "The question of whether alcohol is directly hepatoxic or whether it is indirectly hepatoxic by interfering with nutrition and metabolic processes is not yet answered."*

While the precise role of alcohol in causing cirrhosis may officially rank as a scientific controversy, doctors and researchers overwhelmingly accept a connection. They point to statistics: cirrhosis is seven times as common in alcoholics as it is in nonalcoholics; the risk of developing the disease is related both directly and linearly to the duration and magnitude of alcoholic intake; and the incidence of cirrhosis plummets whenever supplies of alcohol diminish. Before wine was rationed in France during World War II, cirrhosis mortality in Paris was 35 per 100,000 inhabitants. Between 1942 and 1947, when supplies were limited to one liter per week per person, mortality dropped at first by half and then by four fifths to 6 per 100,000. "There can

---

* *American Journal of Clinical Nutrition* (June 1974).

be no doubt that excessive consumption of alcoholic beverages is a cause of hepatic cirrhosis," F. A. Whitlock, a professor of psychiatry at the University of Queensland, Australia, wrote. "Highly significant correlations between rising and falling consumption and cirrhosis death rates over a period of years have been demonstrated. Similarly, differences between countries in annual per capita consumption correlate positively and significantly with cirrhosis deaths. The higher rates of male than female deaths from this cause, the known heavier consumption of alcohol by men, and the sharply increased death rate from cirrhosis in middle life, when many alcoholics deteriorate in physical and mental health, all point to the overriding importance of alcohol as a cause of hepatic cirrhosis."*

The most important evidence of all, perhaps, is a body of research that many believe puts to rest the argument that malnutrition, and not alcohol, is the cause of cirrhosis. That research was the product of a study undertaken by Charles S. Lieber, director of the Alcohol Research and Treatment Center at the Bronx Veterans Administration Medical Center. Lieber initially began to question the malnutrition theory after treating alcoholics who had developed liver disease in spite of the fact that they had maintained a nutritious diet. "In the late 1950's I therefore began to wonder whether alcohol might exert direct toxic effect on the liver," he stated. "Belief in the exclusively nutritional theory was leading many physicians to advise alcoholic patients that normal liver function could be maintained in spite of heavy alcohol consumption as long as the diet was adequate. If that was not true, it would be good to know it."

The first leg of Lieber's experiment was to study the effect of ethanol on volunteers who for eighteen days drank six drinks a day—approximately 10 ounces of 86-

---

* *Quarterly Journal of Studies on Alcohol*, 35:586–605 (1974).

proof alcohol—while maintaining a low-fat, high-protein diet. Lieber characterized that dosage as "rather moderate" in that none of the volunteers showed any clinical signs of intoxication; each person's blood alcohol level was below the legal limit for drinking and driving. Yet on that regimen, there was an average eightfold rise in liver fat. "Here was the characteristic 'fatty liver,' the first (and typically reversible) stage of liver disease," Lieber noted.*

The next leg of the experiment was to verify the effects and study the mechanisms by reproducing them in experimental animals. Lieber put a group of rats on a nutritious diet that had been fortified with alcohol. Just as the humans had, the rats developed fatty livers.

The final leg of the experiment was to put sixteen baboons on a diet in which alcohol comprised 50 percent of the calories, and to compare them to the same number of baboons on an alcohol-free diet with the same amount of calories. Results: All sixteen of the animals on the alcohol-rich diet developed fatty livers, five developed alcoholic hepatitis and six eventually developed cirrhosis. The control animals exhibited no liver abnormalities whatever. Said Lieber: "The rat and baboon experiments demonstrated clearly that severe liver injury can be produced by prolonged heavy ingestion of alcohol even when the diet is good."

But how prolonged, and how heavy? To find out whether short-term alcohol intake would injure the livers of normal nonalcoholic persons, Lieber and a colleague, Emanuel Rubin, performed another experiment with twelve volunteers, four women and eight men between nineteen and thirty-two years of age. Most of the subjects were students; all were well-nourished. One was an abstainer, all the others extremely light drinkers. None had taken a drink for two weeks prior to the experiment. The subjects were

* Scientific American (March 1976).

divided into four groups, fed different diets and given eight doses of alcohol each day, beginning at six-thirty in the morning and ending at midnight. Groups 1 and 2 drank between 68 and 170 grams a day—roughly six to twelve drinks—for a period of six to fourteen days. Groups 3 and 4 drank between 180 and 270 grams, the equivalent of thirteen to nineteen drinks—an effort to reproduce the effects of weekend drinking—for two days. Because the doses were spaced out over such a long period, not even the heaviest drinkers became intoxicated, although all of them experienced headaches and nausea. The effects on their livers, however, were marked.

"It is . . . clear that alcohol can rapidly produce liver injury when taken in amounts equivalent to those consumed not only by recognized alcoholic persons but by many 'social drinkers' as well," Lieber and Rubin commented in an article describing their experiment.* "The blood alcohol levels in this study fluctuated generally between 20 and 80 milligrams per 100 milliliters, most being about 50 milligrams. In the United States an alcohol blood level of 100 or 150 milligrams per 100 milliliters (depending on the state) is considered legal evidence of intoxication . . . Almost all samples in this study were below even the strictest limit. Moreover, although episodes of euphoria occurred in some subjects, there was no sign of gross intoxication, such as slurred speech or ataxic gait. This finding is particularly pertinent to the not infrequent problem of fatty liver and alcoholic hepatitis in successful business and professional people, who are socially not considered alcoholics, but whose business and social contacts almost invariably involve consumption of alcoholic beverages. The data show that a person need never have been drunk to sustain alcohol-induced liver injury."

* *New England Journal of Medicine* (April 18, 1968).

In the past, the minimum amount of alcohol consumption researchers had associated with liver damage was 80 grams a day. "That's not an unusual amount," Dr. Lieber contends—two restaurant drinks at lunch, two drinks at home before dinner, and two glasses of wine with dinner will put the drinker over the threshold. "In some individuals this will cause liver damage. In many it will not. In any case, the person who's incurring the liver damage will not be aware of it," Dr. Lieber says.

To many researchers today, however, the 80-grams-a-day threshold—five to six drinks—is now considered high, particularly for women.

Of all the efforts to determine the relationship of alcohol consumption to cirrhosis of the liver, the one that stands out in the minds of many alcohol researchers is a study performed in France a decade ago and reported in the *International Journal of Epidemiology*.* Data for the study were collected by the Department of Nutrition of the National Institute of Health and Medical Research and by the International Agency for Research on Cancer. One hundred and eighty-four male cirrhotic patients hospitalized in the *département* of Ille-et-Vilaine in Brittany between January 1972 and July 1973 were compared to 778 controls, representing a sample of the total population of the *département*. In order to overcome the difficulties of identifying cirrhosis in its early stages, the researchers chose only those advanced cases with ascites, a painful accumulation of fluids in the peritoneal cavity that is obvious to both the patient and the physician and is the most common cause of death in cirrhotic patients.

The researchers, George Pequignot, Albert J. Tuyns and J. L. Berta, were able to establish to their satisfaction

* Vol. 7, No. 2 (1978).

that 93 percent of the cases of cirrhosis were related to alcohol consumption. They divided the patients into categories based on their daily level of consumption, with increments of 20 grams of absolute alcohol—the equivalent of one-quarter liter of 10% wine, a pint of 5% beer or 2 ounces of straight whiskey. For those drinking between 21 and 40 grams a day the "relative risk" of contracting ascitic cirrhosis was calculated as 3.1 times greater than it was for those drinking 20 grams or less. For those drinking between 41 and 60 grams a day it was 6.2 times greater; and for those drinking 61 to 80 grams it was 13.8 times greater. Above the 80-grams-a-day figure, the risk rose precipitously, to almost 30 times greater for the 81–100 category, 41 times greater for the 101–120 category, 124.3 times greater for the 121–140 category, and 659.3 times greater for the 141+ category.

"The determination of a 'safe level' (a qualitative concept) of alcohol intake as to cirrhosis of the liver is out of the question in a study of this nature," the researchers noted. "What can be safely stated, however, is that if everyone in this particular population consumed no more than 40 grams per day, the total number of ascitic cirrhosis would have been 20 percent of what has been observed; in other words, four out of five cases could have been avoided."

In a corollary study of women in Ille-et-Vilaine, the relative risk of cirrhosis for those drinking between 21 and 40 grams of absolute alcohol a day was found to be 6 times greater than it was for those drinking 20 grams or less. For those drinking 41 to 60 grams the risk was 51 times greater, and for those drinking more than 60 grams the risk was 810 times greater.

". . . it is becoming increasingly evident that [alcoholic beverages] have toxic effects for various viscera beginning with doses which are on the order of from one-fourth to one-half a liter of wine in females and from one-half to one liter of wine in males," the French researchers concluded. "It is generally well known that habitual drinkers of these quantities have a metabolic adaptation such that they usually experience no objectively discernible psychotropic effect. It is also possible that the metabolic adaptation of the liver to increasing doses of alcohol is ultimately the cause of cirrhosis."

Dr. Pequignot, sixty-two, director of research at France's National Institute of Health and Medical Research, has been investigating the relationship of alcohol consumption to cirrhosis since the 1950s, a time, he recalls, when the culpability of alcohol was completely contested in the United States. "In France, we never had any doubts. All the cirrhotic patients were drinkers." Neither Pequignot nor his co-worker, Dr. Tuyns, can understand how people can deny the relationship of alcohol to cirrhosis. Says Dr. Tuyns, a Belgian epidemiologist in his late fifties: "In a country where hepatitis is widespread and people don't drink, most cirrhosis will be associated with hepatitis. In a country where there is little hepatitis and most people drink, most cirrhosis will be associated with alcohol." Pequignot believes today that two out of three cirrhotic cases can be ascribed to alcohol when consumption reaches levels of 21 to 40 grams a day—the equivalent of one and a half to three drinks. "There is an increase of risk beginning with twenty grams," Dr. Tuyns says. "Of that we are sure." Sixteen of the 268 cirrhotics the researchers identified in a recent study in Calvados had been regular consumers of between 20 and 40 grams a day. When consumption rises above 20 grams, the increase in risk for males is 2.9 times and for women 3.2 times what it would be if they drank less than 20 grams a day. Below 20 grams a day, the increase in risk is so small that it is not worth considering.

Does this mean that if you drink more than 20 grams a day you're going to develop cirrhosis? Not at all, the researchers respond. It just means that of 1,000 people who drink more than 20 grams a day there will be a higher incidence of cirrhosis than in individuals who drink less than 20 grams a day.

Despite his more recent findings, Dr. Pequignot continues to be cited for much earlier work in which he placed the level of risk at 80 grams a day. He is at least as critical of that work as were French epidemiologists three decades ago when it was performed. He had made a simple mistake, Pequignot believes; he had divided the world into those who drank more than 80 grams and those who drank less. It was a tradition in France to do that, principally because a liter of wine contains approximately 80 grams, and he was "trapped" in that tradition. "If I speak of a lower threshold now, it is because I have made progress," he allowed in Paris in the summer of 1982. "If I didn't find it the first time, it's because I didn't look for it."

Cancer is an all-encompassing term for some hundred diseases, all of which share one major characteristic: the rampant multiplication of cells. The cells create a tumor which, if not checked, invades the healthy tissue around it, destroying it in the process. The malignant cells can also pass via the blood and lymph—the fluid that bathes body cells—to other parts of the body, where new cancers begin.

Cancer is another drinker's hazard. Clinical evidence for the association between alcohol and cancer goes back at least to 1836, when a Boston surgeon named J. C. Warren, describing a case of cancer of the tongue in a man who chewed tobacco, noted that "predisposition . . . was generated by the long use of ardent spirits." Since then, enormous quantities of clinical and epidemiological evidence have established that drinkers contract cancer more frequently than nondrinkers, more or less in direct proportion to the amounts they drink. In the past, cancer related to drinking was thought to be a risk exclusively for heavy drinkers; recent epidemiological studies, however, have demonstrated that the hazards exist also in consumption ranges generally ascribed to social drinking. One researcher, Gerhard Freund of the College of Medicine of the University of Florida, believes that the relationship of social drinking to cancer has yet to be told. "There may be an important role of moderate alcohol consumption in cancer biology that is not presently recognized by epidemiological studies because cancers and moderate alcohol consumption are very prevalent in the general population," he stated in an abstract of an article in the July 1979 issue of *Cancer Research.* "Moderate, social alcohol use could potentially either suppress or enhance the induction, growth, spread, or therapy of cancers."

While most authorities agree that a person who drinks increases his risk of cancer, there is no certainty among them as to precisely what role alcohol plays. Numbers of them speculate that alcohol irritates body tissues. Others propose that alcohol bathes and washes the body cells to such a degree that they are made vulnerable to known carcinogens, like those found in tobacco and even in the alcoholic beverage itself. Asbestos fibers, for example, have been found in beer, wine, sherry and vermouth. A few years ago the Food and Drug Administration threw a scare into the nation's beer drinkers and most of its brewers when it discovered nitrosamines in unsafe amounts in a number of popular brands. Nitrosamines, administered in relatively large amounts, have produced esophageal cancer in animals. They are the same carcinogens thought to be produced by frying bacon. Their formation in the beer was attributed to the excessive heat used to dry malt. The brewers quickly substituted a revised method for drying the malt, using a cooler flame for a long period, and appeared to get rid of the problem. But the question of carcinogens persists. Said the NIAAA in 1978 in its third report on *Alcohol and Health*: "All alcoholic beverages contain chemicals in addition to ethanol. The carcinogenic property of an alcoholic beverage therefore may involve other constituents of the beverage, or alcohol and the other constituents may act synergistically in eliciting the cancer."

Is alcohol itself a carcinogen? Many researchers think not. "Some substances might be promoters of carcinogenesis, although they themselves are not cancer causing. Alcohol might well be one such agent," William Lijinsky, a researcher with the chemical carcinogenesis program at the Frederick Cancer Research Center in Frederick, Maryland, observes. But the NIAAA appears to believe otherwise. "In liver cancer, alcohol alone can function as the carcinogenic agent," it noted in the third report. "Baboons fed purified alcohol have been shown to develop cirrhosis, and cirrhosis appears to be a sufficient condition for cancer development."

Yet another theory about the relationship of alcohol consumption to cancer is that it helps to produce or reinforce emotional states that are thought to be antecedents of the disease because of the profound manner in which they can disturb the body's chemistry. Although many people drink in an effort to be rid of depression, the ultimate effect of alcohol, if taken in sufficient quantities, may be to reinforce their depression, and thus the irritation to their system.

In spite of the lack of an adequate explanation, most researchers and physicians proceed on the assumption that a relationship exists between alcohol and cancer. "Although the mechanism of cancer causation is unknown, heavy alcohol consumption has been related to an increased risk of cancer at various sites in the human body, particularly malignancies involving the mouth, pharynx, larynx and esophagus," the fourth *Alcohol and Health* report noted. A national cancer survey of some 7,500 cancer cases, reported in 1977, revealed "a significant positive association between alcohol intake and cancers of the oral cavity and larynx and less striking positive associations between alcohol and cancers of the esophagus, stomach, colon, liver, breast, thyroid gland, and malignant melanoma. The relative odds were usually higher in females, who also differed from males by a positive association between alcohol and rectal cancer. Upper digestive tract cancers were found to occur with greater frequency in men, blacks, lower socioeconomic groups, and with increasing urbanization and increasing age (35–70 years)."

In 1977 the NIAAA published the results of a study performed by Albert Tuyns, the Belgian epidemiologist, to determine the annual incidence rates in the United States for selected cancer sites: the tongue, mouth, oropharynx, hypopharynx, esophagus, liver and larynx. Analyzing information collected by other researchers on various population groups in California, Connecticut, Iowa, Michigan, New Mexico, New York, Utah and Puerto Rico, Tuyns concluded that "the proportion of cancer cases at sites known to be associated with alcohol consumption is approximately 8 percent in most population groups in the United States." Inasmuch as some 700,000 new cases of cancer are reported each year, alcohol could possibly be incriminated in some way in 56,000 of these cases.

In a review of the studies dealing with alcohol and cancer, Tuyns observed: "Despite certain disadvantages, the remarkable feature of all these studies is the consistency of their results: as compared with the normal 'general' population, heavy consumers of alcohol show an excess of mortality both in general and for cancer as a whole. There is always a marked excess for sites of mouth and pharynx, larynx, esophagus, liver and lung. For the same sites, the figures are always lower than 'normal' among abstinent religious groups such as Mormons and Seventh Day Adventists."*

In the past, less than heavy consumption of alcohol had not been linked to cancer except in a few studies. In 1965, researchers had reported an association between the consumption of 35 grams of absolute alcohol—between two and three drinks—per day and cancers of the mouth and pharynx, when the drinking was combined with smoking. It remained for Tuyns and his colleagues, George Pequignot among them, to establish that the risk of cancer existed among less than heavy consumers even after adjustments for smoking. The researchers found the same profound synergistic relationship between cancer and smoking reported by others, but they were also able to establish the likely role of each in producing cancer of the esophagus.

The study of esophageal cancer was done in the same department in France as the study of cirrhosis. The choice of research site was not accidental. Whereas, in most countries, the prevalence of the disease was 3 to 4 per 100,000 population, in France it was 16 per 100,000, and in one area—Brittany and Normandy—it was 25 to 30 per 100,000. When Tuyns and his co-workers arrived on the scene, they found an even starker comparison than they had anticipated. Four departments in Brittany, all of them on the English Channel, had a rate of 50 to 60 per 100,000 population—approximately 20 times what it was among inhabitants of the English coast just across the water. "That was a situation worth investigating," Dr. Tuyns recalled during a 1982 visit in Lyon, where he is affiliated with the World Health Organization's International Agency on Research on Cancer. "We felt that we might put our finger on the factors involved."

* *Alcohol Health and Research World* (Summer 1978).

The esophagus is a simple tube through which food passes from the mouth to the stomach. Cancer of the esophagus has for a long time been associated with heavy drinking and smoking. What Tuyns and his colleagues wanted to do was establish just how much drinking and smoking was required to produce the disease.

The study involved 200 men who had been admitted to hospitals in Ille-et-Vilaine with the disease, and 1,640 control subjects consisting of a representative sample of the adult population twenty-five years and older. Once again, drinking was measured in units of 20 grams, which corresponds to one-quarter liter of 10% wine a day. The result: "As compared to the small consumers who did not drink more than 20 grams per day, the risk is nearly four times greater for the class that consumed from 41 to 60 grams and 20 times higher for those who drank more than 100 grams."

The study indicated that both alcohol and tobacco bore individual risks, as previous studies had shown. An individual who drank 40 grams a day of absolute alcohol or less and smoked 20 cigarettes or more a day had a relative risk 5.1 times that of a person in the same drinking category who smoked 9 cigarettes a day or less. A person who smoked 20 cigarettes or more a day and drank 80 grams or more of absolute alcohol had a relative risk 44.4 times greater than someone in the lowest consumption category.

"It's not true that you must smoke *and* drink to get esophageal cancer," Dr. Tuyns remarks. "If you smoke a lot, it increases your chances of getting esophageal cancer even if you don't drink. If you drink a lot, you increase your chances even if you don't smoke. If you do both, you multiply your chances. If you drink three and smoke three, your risk isn't six, it's nine."

Had factors other than alcohol and tobacco played a role in the causation of this disease? The authors acknowledged that there are regions in the world, such as northern Iran, where the incidence of esophageal cancer is very high even though alcohol and tobacco are scarcely consumed at all. After two verification processes to discover if some other factor was present, they concluded: "Without excluding the possibility of exceptional cases caused by other known agents (as for example, caustic chemical agents), it seems that in the case of Ille-et-Vilaine, at least, alcohol and tobacco can explain nearly all of the cases of esophageal cancer."

On the basis of their study, the researchers projected what might happen if "everyone accepted" certain limits on daily consumption. The two most striking results were achieved with drinking "limited" to 40 grams a day. With that amount of consumption and no decrease in smoking, the number of cases of esophageal cancer in France would diminish by 70 percent. If the 40-gram alcohol consumption were maintained at the same time that consumption of tobacco were limited to 9 grams a day, the number of cases would be only 13.4 percent of current totals. Said Tuyns: "One argument sometimes used in France to encourage people to drink and smoke less is that if French males in Brittany smoked and drank as little as do their spouses, they would probably enjoy the same esophageal cancer rate, which is one-twentieth their own."

Another study, this an American one on oral cancer related to alcohol consumption, also appeared to implicate social drinking in the upper ranges. Oral cancer accounts for some 4 percent of all cancers occurring each year in the United States, and some 8,000 deaths. It is found most frequently in men over forty. In the past, most of the blame for oral cancer was laid to heavy smoking. What the Americans found was that drinking could be a much greater risk factor than had previously been suspected. "Although our study confirms the synergistic effect of alcohol and tobacco, the results differ in several respects from other studies investigating the role of alcohol in oral cancer," the authors of the study wrote. "Our data indicate that for someone who smokes and drinks, doubling the alcohol consumption leads to a much greater risk of oral cancer than doubling the cigarette consumption."

Although the American researchers—Dr. Arthur Mashberg, chief of oral and maxillofacial surgery at Veterans Administration Medical Center in East Orange, New Jersey, and clinical professor of surgery at New Jersey Medical School, and Lawrence Garfinkel, vice president for epidemiology and statistics of the American Cancer Society—referred to "heavy" drinking in their report, their heavy-drinking cutoff point was well within the social drinking range.

Those patients who drank less than 6 ounces of whiskey or its equivalent a day had an oral-cancer risk 3.3 times greater than those who didn't drink; those who consumed between 6 and 9 ounces of whiskey or its equivalent increased their risk to 15.2, the researchers found.

Paradoxically, among those drinking 10 or more ounces of whiskey or its equivalent—the highest drinking category —the risk of oral cancer *dropped* to 10.6. Much of that drop, the researchers surmised, was accounted for by the high number of whiskey drinkers in the group that drank the most, whereas the group immediately below that was heavily weighted with beer and wine drinkers. On the basis of this result, the researchers hypothesized that beer and wine drinkers might be at greater risk for oral cancer than those who drink whiskey.

This hypothesis raises a difficult question: Which form of alcoholic beverage is least likely to produce cancer? In their study of esophageal cancer, Tuyns, Pequignot and their colleagues established that those who habitually drank stronger beverages were at greater risk than those who drank lighter ones—the exact opposite of what the oral-cancer researchers found. Other studies in the past ten years have appeared to correlate beer consumption with cancer of the rectum. Two separate efforts have been undertaken to test that correlation, with totally contradictory results. One study was done on Danish brewery workers who had been affiliated with the Brewery Workers' Union between 1939 and 1963. The workers received an average of six pints of free beer a day, approximately four times higher than amounts consumed by the average Dane. An analysis of deaths indicated a higher mortality rate and a higher incidence of cancer (as well as gastrointestinal diseases) among the brewery workers than among the general population, but no excess incidence of cancer of the colon or rectum. A second study, however, this one of blue-collar workers at a Dublin, Ireland, brewery, showed 77 percent more cases of cancer of the rectum than in corresponding populations.

On the basis of what is known to date, then, there doesn't seem to be a clear answer to that difficult question of which drink is the "safest." Nor, in spite of everything that *is* known, does there seem to be an answer to the role of alcohol in cancer. "Drinking is deeply enmeshed in our social fabric and is intimately associated with a wide variety of behaviors relevant to cancer," Robin Room of Berkeley's Alcohol Research Group wrote in the July 1979 issue of *Cancer Research.* "Consider the man at the ball park, drinking beer and watching the great American pastime. The beer may facilitate cancer or even carry carcinogens such as asbestos fibers. If he does not drink beer, maybe he will drink soft drinks (which may themselves contain carcinogens). If it is a sunny day, he is presumably exposing himself to an increased risk of skin cancer. Along with the beer or soft drinks, he will probably eat the ball park hotdogs, complete with nitrites . . ."

When we consider that the cause of cancer is still unknown, as is a means to prevent it, it should not be surprising that the precise role of alcohol is still undetermined.

But the evidence of a relationship—even at social-drinking levels—is so suggestive that it must be treated with respect.

Let us return now to the subject of alcohol and the heart. As we've seen, drinking might produce some heart-related benefits. But it can also produce some problems.

Perhaps the most widespread, as well as vexatious, medical problem associated with alcohol and the cardiovascular system is hypertension, which is a factor in a large proportion of premature deaths. Hypertension is the name given to elevation of the blood pressure, especially the diastolic pressure, and to the arterial disease characterized by this condition. Think of what happens to the flow of water in a garden hose when the nozzle is tightened, and you will understand exactly what is happening in the body's arteries. The greater the blood pressure, the greater the impediment to blood flow and the harder the heart must pump to move the blood through the body. *The Manual of Medical Therapeutics*, a reference book popular among clinicians, lists hypertension as the major cause in 75 percent of congestive heart failure cases, and in 25 percent of cerebral hemorrhages.

One in four Americans suffers from hypertension of some sort, although most of them are unaware of it. Anything they might do to raise their blood pressure even further would obviously not be in their interest. The immediate, or acute, effect of alcohol is to raise the blood pressure with the first drinks, and to lower it after heavier quantities have been drunk. The long-term, or chronic, effect is to raise blood pressure on a quasi-permanent basis. Most studies appear to show that anything more than two drinks a day raises blood pressure in the latter fashion.

The connection between alcohol and hypertension first appeared in the 1950s, in a study made at the Western Electric Company in Chicago. Male workers were given a free medical examination and were then followed for several years. Hypertension increased in proportion to their average daily consumption of alcohol: 20 percent of abstainers, 26.9 percent of two-to-three-a-day drinkers, and 47.4 percent of six-or-more-a-day drinkers were hypertensive.

Subsequent studies confirmed the relationship of alcohol consumption to hypertension. The benchmark Framingham Study showed a doubled prevalence of hypertension among persons drinking 60 ounces or more of ethanol a month compared to persons drinking less than 30 ounces a month. In that study, the researchers equated 60 ounces of ethanol to 16 ounces (one pint) of table wine, five beers or 5 ounces of 80-proof spirits a day. Thirty ounces would of course translate to half those amounts.

The largest study ever done on the relationship of blood pressure to alcohol use involved some 84,000 members of the Kaiser-Permanente Health Care Program in the San Francisco Bay Area and was reported in 1977. "Men who usually took two or fewer drinks per day had blood pressures similar to those of nondrinkers," the report noted. "Women who took two drinks or less per day had slightly lower blood pressures than nondrinkers. Men and women who consumed three drinks or more daily had higher systolic and diastolic pressures than nondrinkers or persons who took two drinks or less per day . . . The difference in mean blood pressure translated into a doubled prevalence of hypertension . . . in white men and women who took six drinks or more daily compared to nondrinkers or users of two or fewer drinks daily. Among black men and women the prevalence of hypertension among users of three or more drinks daily was increased by approximately 50 percent. The alcohol-blood pressure link was independent of age, sex, race, cigarette smoking, coffee use, past 'heavy' drinking, adiposity (weight/height index), educational attainment, or regular salt use. Regular daily use of three drinks or more was found to be associated with

an increased risk of hypertension but use of smaller amounts
of alcohol did not appear to carry such a risk."

A good deal remains unclear about the relationship between drinking and hypertension. Does high blood pressure precede heavier alcohol use or vice versa? Is it possible
that the higher blood pressure is caused by stress rather
than by alcohol? Are heavier drinkers confounding the
data by not drinking before a physical examination, a stress-
producing practice that might elevate their blood pressure
even more than if they'd been drinking? Are ethnic patterns, personality and diet somehow involved? And what
of "psychosocial stress," which increases thirst and elevates
blood pressure? "For all these reasons, a causal relation between alcohol use and hypertension is *not* proved," Dr.
Klatsky and his colleagues noted. "Yet, considering all the
evidence, we feel that it is a strong possibility."

"The most serious problem probably resides in the sub-
group of people who don't handle triglycerides well," Dr.
Jacob Brody of the National Institute on Aging asserts.
(Triglycerides are the major fat in blood.) "They're usually
overweight, they've got a sedentary existence, they've got
mild hypertension and they may even be smokers. Adding
to their triglyceride level by any amount is presenting them
with an additional risk factor." What alcohol does is to add
a carbohydrate load, which, in turn, increases triglycerides.
"A certain percentage of these people will be pushed over
the brink," Dr. Brody contends. "Doctors scream to them,
'Don't smoke, don't smoke, don't smoke.' They should do
the same thing about alcohol.

"Cardiovascular events constitute fifty percent of all
deaths. Hypertension could be the result of a heart condition but it could also cause a heart condition. If you're
speaking of only one percent of deaths caused by this condition, the number is still gigantic. When people do studies
of large numbers of people who had heart attacks they find
that most of them had high cholesterol. However, a sig-

nificant portion have high triglycerides. The problem in either case is that people are consuming too much and having problems metabolizing it. Whatever it is, it enters into the same pool and clogs the arteries. If you're one of those people who don't metabolize triglycerides very well, a drink is worse than taking an extra piece of cake. Anything that will add to the triglycerides burden is pushing the system in the direction it shouldn't be pushed."

In a study undertaken in 1977 at Helsinki's University Hospital, Finnish researchers found that moderate consumption of alcohol in the evening "markedly increased" serum triglyceride levels. "In most cases, the elevated triglyceride levels persisted until 8 the next morning," a report of the study recounted. "These findings indicate that moderate drinking, either occasional or constant, may be a common cause of hypertriglyceridemia."

All such facts and study results seem to heighten an anomaly that confronts alcohol researchers: the same substance appears to extend life in some instances, and shorten it in others. "While most of the population studies suggest that drinkers suffer fewer major coronary events, studies of problem drinkers and alcoholics show the opposite," the NIAAA's fourth report noted. Says Charles Kaelber, chief of the NIAAA's Laboratory of Epidemiology and Population Studies: "We may have to live with a certain amount of ambiguity, because there's no reason to expect alcohol to have a single effect on the heart and blood vessels."

There are several reasons why. The first, Kaelber explains, is that alcohol has "multiple sites of action" within the cardiovascular system, which means that it could possibly affect different cells in different ways. Second, the effects of alcohol are "dose dependent," meaning that large doses might affect the body very differently than small ones. The third cause of variation is the drinker himself, and the degree to which the peculiarities of his cardiovascular system will affect his response to alcohol.

"The relation of alcohol habits to each cardiovascular condition must be considered separately," Drs. Klatsky and Friedman, and their colleague Abraham Siegelaub of Oakland's Kaiser-Permanente Medical Center, noted. "Thus, the apparent role of alcohol in cardiomyopathy, hypertension, angina pectoris, myocardial infarction, or sudden cardiac death consists of features unique to each condition. A simplistic view that alcohol is 'good for the heart' or 'bad for the heart' is inappropriate. Furthermore, the relation of low or relatively small amounts of alcohol to a particular cardiovascular condition may be different from that of large amounts."*

For all these reasons, even those who are investigating the positive contribution moderate drinking might make to health take a cautious stance, and few, if any, would counsel those who don't drink to start. That conservative approach was reflected in the NIAAA's fourth report to Congress (January 1981). "Caution in interpreting the reports on the presumably beneficial effects of moderate alcohol [use] is clearly warranted," the NIAAA summed up. "Based on present information, encouraging the use of alcohol to reduce the likelihood of occurrence or recurrence of heart disease must be questioned because it has been noted that any potential benefits to be derived appear to be outweighed by the attendant risks associated with increasing alcohol consumption."

* *Alcoholism: Clinical and Experimental Research* (January 1979).

7 · The Case for Caution II

Birth Defects and Synergistics

In Canada some years ago, a pregnant woman went into labor while in an alcoholic stupor, a condition she had apparently been in for two months. When the baby was born, the doctor could smell alcohol on its breath; eighteen hours after delivery the infant began to exhibit classical withdrawal symptoms. The symptoms continued for several days, and it was ten days before the infant was completely normal.

The possibility that a woman's drinking during pregnancy might adversely affect her child has been voiced since the time of Aristotle, and doctors have known for at least a century that alcohol passes from the bloodstream of the pregnant woman to the fetus via the placenta. Yet it has only been in the last decade that the possible consequences of this transfer have been identified and become the focus of intense concern. The most disquieting news of all is that while the fetal alcohol syndrome (FAS) was once associated exclusively with alcoholic mothers and their offspring, there are indications that even small amounts of alcohol imbibed by pregnant women—including those who aren't aware they've conceived—could produce some damage.

"Fetal alcohol effects—a range of physical and mental problems in the newborn child—may result from a pregnant woman's social drinking in the same way fetal alcohol syndrome can be caused by heavy drinking," the *Maryland State Medical Journal* cautioned in a November 1980 article. "One or several of the conditions characteristic of FAS"—prenatal and postnatal growth deficiencies, abnormalities of head and face, joint and limb problems, cardiac defects, delayed development and mental deficiency—"may be present in a child who has suffered fetal alcohol effects." Hyperactivity and learning disabilities could also result from drinking during pregnancy, the article noted.

What is it about alcohol that can produce the fetal alcohol syndrome or other alcohol-related birth defects? The explanation with the most currency focuses on acetaldehyde, one of alcohol's byproducts, which may possibly be poorly metabolized, in turn, by certain women. The fetuses of mothers who could metabolize acetaldehyde well would be unaffected by normal drinking such as wine with meals, whereas mothers who could not metabolize acetaldehyde well would harm the fetus and damage the placenta even by drinking small amounts of alcohol. Cutting down alcohol intake after the damage had occurred would be useless. Whatever the specific cause turns out to be, the role of alcohol, generally, in birth defects is now accepted by many scientists.

French researchers comparing the outcome of more than 9,000 pregnancies found a significantly higher incidence of premature placental separation, stillbirth and low birth rate associated with mothers who drank more than 1.5 ounces of absolute alcohol a day—about three drinks—than among mothers who drank less than that.

In a study at Boston City Hospital during the mid-seventies, 322 infants were examined by a pediatric neurologist who had no knowledge of their mothers' drinking habits or obstetric history. Congenital and growth abnormalities and jitteriness in the infants born to heavy-drinking women were twice as prevalent as among infants born to moderate- and light-drinking mothers. Infants born to heavy-drinking mothers who had continued to drink during pregnancy slept less well than the infants of heavy-drinking mothers who had modified their intake during pregnancy, and they were much more restless and awakened much more often than infants of mothers who had never been heavy drinkers. "These disruptions are important because basic temporal organization of the nervous system is developing through interaction with the caregiver during the first weeks of life," Dr. Henry L. Rosett and Lyn Weiner, the director and associate director, respectively, of the Fetal Alcohol Education Program at Boston University Medical Center, commented in an article. "Disturbances in an infant's regulation of sleep-awake states may have far-reaching detrimental effects on the quality of mother-child interactions."*

For the purpose of this study, "heavy drinking" was defined as at least forty-five drinks a month, with five or more drinks on some occasions—a description that would fit almost any woman who is accustomed to having a drink or two at dinnertime and attending "wet" social events from time to time.

In a study of members of a health maintenance organization in Seattle, Washington, Dr. Ruth E. Little found that women who drank an average of 1 ounce of absolute alcohol a day before pregnancy gave birth to babies whose average weight was 3.2 ounces less than infants born to mothers who didn't drink. Women who drank the same amounts late in their pregnancies gave birth to babies whose weight was 5.6 ounces below the average weight of babies whose mothers didn't drink. Said Little: "This suggests the possibility of a continuum of effects over the alcohol con-

* *CMA Journal* (July 15, 1981).

sumption spectrum, with minor alterations in growth at one end and fetal alcohol syndrome at the other extreme." Cautioning that inferences be drawn with care, particularly since " 'nice fat babies' aren't necessarily the healthiest," Little noted nonetheless that "reduction in birth weight with moderate alcohol use may represent minimal damage on a spectrum of growth retardation. The present study merely opens the door to this major question."*

Through that door a year later came several of Little's colleagues at the University of Washington, James W. Hanson and David W. Smith, both medical doctors, and Ann Pytkowicz Streissguth, a Ph.D. An article they co-authored implicated moderate as well as high levels of alcohol intake during early pregnancy in "alterations of growth and morphogenesis in the fetus." Noting that "information on fetal hazards arising from moderate or low levels of maternal alcohol consumption is unavailable in man," the authors reported on a study undertaken at two Seattle hospitals in which mothers were predominantly white, middle-class and well-educated. Among the 163 mothers whose infants were chosen for examination, sixteen drank 2 or more ounces of absolute alcohol a day prior to learning they were pregnant; three of the sixteen delivered children with FAS features. Fifty-four of the mothers consumed between 1 and 2 ounces of absolute alcohol a day prior to learning they were pregnant; six of those mothers delivered children with FAS features.

On the basis of their findings, the authors proposed that "a crude dose-response curve relating maternal alcohol intake to outcome of pregnancy" could now be visualized. "These data suggest that the risk of having a newborn child with FAS increases proportionately with the average daily intake. If average maternal ingestion is less than one ounce of absolute alcohol per day, the apparent risk for

* *American Journal of Public Health* (December 1977).

abnormalities appears to be low. In the range of one to two ounces of absolute alcohol per day, the risk may approach 10 percent. Among the women who drank an average of two or more ounces of ethanol daily, 19 percent had infants who were considered abnormal. In each of these latter instances, however, the reported average daily maternal alcohol consumption was greater than five ounces. Previous reports have suggested that in chronic alcoholic women the risk of producing a clinically abnormal child may be 40 percent or more."

Summing up, the authors said: "These data provide a strong reason to suspect that moderate levels of alcohol consumption during early pregnancy can have an adverse effect on the fetus. Although the mothers of the two infants who had the most obvious features of FAS both drank heavily preceding and during the early stages of pregnancy, six of nine other women who had children with numerous features consistent with a prenatal effect of alcohol had AA [absolute alcohol] scores between 1 and 2. This suggests that at moderate levels of maternal alcohol consumption there are recognizable signs of altered growth and morphogenesis, clinically apparent at the time of birth, in some of the exposed children. The strongest relationship between maternal alcohol consumption and fetal outcome seems to exist for drinking behavior in the month preceding recognition of pregnancy."*

By 1980, FAS reports had surfaced in sufficient number to provoke a warning from the NIAAA. "Given the total evidence available at this time, pregnant women should be particularly conscious of the extent of their drinking," the agency stated. "While safe levels of drinking are unknown, it appears that a risk is established with ingestion of about three ounces of absolute alcohol or six drinks per day. Between one and three ounces, there is still uncertainty but

---

* *Journal of Pediatrics* (March 1978).

caution is advised." One year later, however, the U.S. Surgeon General advised pregnant women, and those attempting to become pregnant, to avoid alcohol altogether. Too little is known about the effects of alcohol to condone any amount, public health officials explained. Said John DeLuca, the then director of the NIAAA: "It's really quite simple—we don't know a safe level. I can't say that one drink is safe and one and a half is not."

Statements in the fourth *Alcohol and Health* report gave a number of clues as to what was behind the stiffer recommendation. "Studies have consistently found that heavier alcohol use during pregnancy is associated with decreased birthweight, greater frequency of spontaneous abortions, and behavioral and neurological effects on neonates," the report said.

The NIAAA noted that while FAS data are not available in the United States, an incidence of one case in every 600 births had been reported in Göteborg, Sweden, and a similar incidence reported in Roubaix, France. "Alcohol consumption during lactation and the consequent effects on nursing infants is also an area of concern," the NIAAA said. "Alcohol readily enters the breast milk, thereby providing alcohol to the nursing infant."

Even drinking fathers might be incriminated in the problem, the NIAAA hinted. It cited one study in which male rats that had consumed alcohol were mated with females that hadn't. Result: a high rate of fetal deaths, and a significant reduction in birth weights.

Like so many other findings in recent years about the apparent dangers inherent in relatively moderate alcohol consumption, the linking of the fetal alcohol syndrome to social-drinking levels has produced an extraordinary degree of controversy.

"We agree that pregnant women who drink large amounts of alcohol (five or more drinks on an occasion) place their children at risk for a variety of abnormalities," Dr. Henry Rosett and his associate Lyn Weiner, wrote in an article. "We disagree that there is adequate evidence that small quantities of alcohol, especially the amounts contained in food and drugs, represent a risk. Consideration of the evidence for a dose response is necessary for a balanced report. Exaggeration of the weak epidemiologic evidence of possible effects from low levels of drinking interferes with acceptance of the strong evidence of major adverse effects from consumption of high doses." In addition, such exaggeration "may cause parents of abnormal children to experience guilt that small amounts of alcoholic beverages caused anomalies that were actually due to other factors."*

Morris Chafetz, founding director of the NIAAA, called the charges "overkill." Many of the incriminating studies, he said, had surveyed mothers and babies after birth, but not before and during pregnancy. For this reason, Chafetz said, it could not be established whether lower birth weights and spontaneous abortions had been caused by alcohol or by other factors such as smoking, stress or poor nutrition. Other critics charged that the warnings were issued on the basis of inconclusive evidence. "We totally dispute those figures," Paul Gavaghan, spokesman for the Distilled Spirits Council of the United States, stated, a stand that was supported by a number of alcohol researchers who rarely find themselves in accord with the industry. One of the most frequent criticisms was that the FAS researchers had gone looking for data to support their assumptions. "Is FAS post facto organization of the data, as some people believe?" one critic wondered. "If you send out a clinician looking for a syndrome and tell him what it looks like and tell him to go find it, he'll find it." There is a hint in the literature, too, that FAS is not a true "syndrome" but rather a collection

* *Pediatrics* (June 1982).

of problems that mirror the kinds of variables associated with racial minorities and lower-class socioeconomic groups —the very kinds of populations heavily represented in some of the samples. Finally, a number of the disorders placed under the FAS umbrella—hyperactivity, learning disability, minimal brain damage, slow development—are speculative in nature, in that no one really understands why they occur, or whether they are more than behavior patterns at the lower end of a normal scale.

To all such charges, those who profess to have identified the syndrome reply "Nonsense." "How on earth are you going to find something if you don't have a general description of what you're looking for," one researcher scoffs. Moreover, the investigators point out, all of the work was well controlled; the researchers looking for physical and mental abnormalities had no idea which mothers drank during pregnancy and which didn't; the mothers' drinking histories were established only after the abnormalities had been identified. And while the jury may still be out on moderate drinking and its relationship to FAS, that's simply a consequence of a lack of sufficient studies, the researchers argue; such studies as exist are extremely suggestive, and animal studies leave little or no doubt.

Even those researchers who consider the human studies inconclusive believe that animal studies make a convincing case, and they point out that as regards the physiological response to alcohol animals aren't all that different from humans. "It's the old story about the jury: the evidence seems conclusive, but are we willing to hang somebody for it?" comments Dr. Steven Schenker of Nashville. For his part, Schenker says, he wouldn't want his wife to drink alcohol while pregnant.

Next, the problem of alcohol and other drugs.

Synergism, the dictionary tells us, is "the joint action of agents, as drugs, that when taken together increase each other's effectiveness." A not inconsiderable part of alcohol's past has been its medicinal use to relieve pain, promote sleep, allay anxiety and otherwise administer to innumerable physical and psychological problems. In the last several decades, hundreds of new drugs have been contrived to perform these and other services in much more specific and efficient ways. We have drugs to combat motion sickness, relieve head colds and repress allergy symptoms, drugs to relax muscles and arrest spasms, drugs to stop itching and alter moods. Every one of these drugs is a competitor of alcohol. Because their use is so widespread today, the competition is an everyday affair for millions of social drinkers, almost all of whom are unaware of the potential dangers of the synergistic result.

"Because alcohol and some of these other drugs work on the same areas of the brain, taking them fairly close together (not necessarily simultaneously) can produce a combined effect much greater than is expected," the National Clearinghouse for Alcohol Information notes. "For example, alcohol and barbiturates in combination can be particularly dangerous, as they increase each others' effects on the central nervous system. Alcohol in combination with any drug that has a depressant effect on the central nervous system likewise represents a special hazard to health and safety—sometimes to life itself. The drug adds to the normal depressant effect of alcohol, further depressing the nervous system that regulates vital bodily functions. Death can result."

There is a second phase to the competition that compounds the problem, the Clearinghouse explains. It has to do with the way our bodies chemically process what we ingest. "If drugs were not metabolized within the body, their effect would continue for the remainder of a person's life. In the metabolic process, drugs are transformed into other substances, which are eventually eliminated through normal bodily functions. The more rapidly a given drug is metabolized, the less impact it has. When drugs are forced to compete with alcohol for processing by the body, one or both are metabolized more slowly. As a result, the effect of the alcohol and/or the drug is exaggerated because it remains active in the blood for an extended period of time."

Two types of drugs probably represent the most widespread problem. The first are antihistamines, which are being used by as many as 40 million Americans. The second are antianxiety drugs, employed on a fairly regular basis by an estimated 20 million Americans. Antihistamines are mild sedatives; they are known principally for their ability to alleviate allergic symptoms, such as sneezing and itching, but they are also a primary ingredient in sleeping pills and cold remedies sold without prescription. Many persons simply employ their antihistamines as sleeping pills whether they're having allergy attacks or not. In whatever form they're used, those normally mild drugs can pack a knockout wallop when used in conjunction with alcohol. Consider the social drinker who's been to a Saturday-night party and consumed a few cocktails, a few glasses of wine and an after-dinner drink. Returning home, he has a sudden attack of hayfever and decides to take two antihistamines before retiring. Depending on the sensitivity of the person, just that combination of drugs could dangerously lower the body processes.

The same can happen with Valium and Librium, now the most widely prescribed drugs in the United States. "Antianxiety drugs and alcohol share several functions," Professor Robert Straus notes. "Both have sedative and tranquilizing effects; it is suspected that they are metabolically competitive, and when combined, they can also produce synergistic effects. Although directions for the use of antianxiety drugs clearly warn against the concomitant use of alcohol, several studies have revealed that most prescribing physicians don't warn their patients and most patients are oblivious to this danger."

The use of alcohol in conjunction with nonlegal drugs is another phenomenon of the last several decades, with even greater potential for danger. Marijuana was introduced by its proponents as a safe and nonaddictive alternative to alcohol. Today it is used increasingly in conjunction with alcohol. "Although, as yet, relatively little is known about alcohol-marijuana interactions, both drugs produce complex central nervous system responses that can affect motor control, reaction time, perception and judgment," Straus observes. "Marijuana has a particular impact on time and space perception. Until the last few years, the marijuana most commonly used in this country was of relatively low toxicity and its potential dangers were not considered serious. This factor has changed, since the importing of much more potent marijuana products has greatly increased the toxicity of the marijuana now available. Since most people are now using more powerful marijuana products more frequently in association with alcohol, the potential for serious problems of marijuana-alcohol interaction appears substantial."

Obviously, the intent of the user and the amount of each drug used are the all-important factors in any synergistic response. When the simultaneous use is deliberate, as in attempts to alter moods or take one's life, the consequences are anticipated. But accidental adverse reactions, in which the possibility of a compounded effect has been entirely overlooked, are much more common, and have been known to occur even after a single drink.

In its 1979 annual report, prepared for the Drug Enforcement Administration and the National Institute on Drug Abuse, the Drug Abuse Warning Network declared that alcohol in combination with other drugs was the most frequent cause of drug-related medical crises in the United States.

8 · The Case for Caution III

The Cognition Controversy

Of all the issues raised in the last decade about the effects of social drinking, none has more immediate relevance or such potential for controversy as the one involving cognition. Researchers have known for years that heavy doses of alcohol can destroy the brain; what has now been suggested is that drinking at moderate levels can impair the drinker's brain power when he is sober. Where other potential problems associated with social drinking might be years in developing, the loss of thinking power is as pertinent as tomorrow morning.

Numbers of studies in recent years appear to show that the more you drink on each occasion, the greater your cognitive inefficiency the following day—your ability to abstract, form concepts, pursue a conceptual startegy or shift from one conceptual strategy to another. It doesn't seem to matter how many years you've been drinking or how frequently you drink. What matters is the *amount* you drink on each occasion. If you drink three drinks each evening, you will be more impaired mentally the following day than if you drink two; if you drink four drinks, you'll be less sharp the following day than if you drink three; and so forth.

The theory advanced to explain this phenomenon is extremely simple: alcohol produces disturbances in the central nervous system that continue even after it has left the bloodstream. The intensity of the disturbances is in direct proportion to the amount of alcohol consumed.

The two persons most closely associated with the issue of cognition, as well as with the controversy in which it's embroiled, are Ernest Noble, the psychiatrist, biochemist and former director of the NIAAA, and Elizabeth Parker, a Canadian-born psychologist currently doing research under the auspices of the NIAAA. In the early 1970s, Parker became associated with Noble at the University of California, Irvine, and it was with him that the research into the effect of social drinking on cognitive powers began. As we've seen, Noble's interest in the question stemmed from attempts to discover the biochemical basis of the damage that occurs in the brain of a chronic alcoholic. In his work with animals he had discovered that small amounts of alcohol impeded protein and RNA-molecule synthesis in the brain, and he began to wonder whether, if alcohol could damage nonaddicted animals in such a manner, it could also damage nonaddicted humans.

The first task Parker and Noble undertook was to determine whether there was some kind of cognitive carry-over to drinking, not simply among alcoholics, as was already known, but among social drinkers as well, and not when they were drinking, but when they were sober. "Before assertions about the innocuous nature of drinking by non-alcoholics can be made," they wrote in a statement of their intent, "studies are needed that explore the effects of drinking on the functions of nonintoxicated social drinkers. In view of the number of studies reporting significant decrements in memory and other cognitive processes in nonalcoholics under moderate levels of intoxication, it seems reasonable to suspect some carry-over effects of alcohol on the intellectual capacities of sober social drinkers as well as sober alcoholics."

Parker and Noble mailed drinking-history questionnaires to 450 men randomly chosen from the telephone book of a suburban California community. Out of the response they chose 102 fairly homogeneous men in order to minimize the influence of potentially confounding variables such as sex, social class, social stability and nutritional circumstances. All of the subjects had finished high school; more than half were educated beyond the college level. All held good jobs; 40 percent were executives or employed in the professions, 24 percent managers and lesser professionals, 35 percent administrators and semiprofessionals, and only one man was a skilled laborer. Ninety-four percent of the men were married and living with their wives. In all, the subjects were a better-than-average cross section of reasonably successful American males, and their drinking habits corresponded to those of successful U.S. males as well. Thirty-six percent were classified as heavy drinkers, 55 percent as light and moderate drinkers, and 9 percent as infrequent drinkers or abstainers.

Each of the men went through a testing that had been used successfully in the past to measure intellectual impairment in alcoholic patients. The first was a test of general intellectual functioning covering vocabulary and abstraction. Another test required them to make a hypothesis about a figure or design, and then reformulate the hypothesis on the basis of feedback. The third test called for sorting cards according to color, form and shape. The final test was a multitrial, free-recall of thirty words. The results, corrected for age: "Neither lifetime consumption nor current frequency of drinking was significantly related to cognitive performance. There was, however, a consistent pattern of significant correlations between current quantity per drinking occasion and test scores, and every significant correlation was in the direction of decreased performance with increased drinking per occasion. The processes of abstraction, adaptive abilities and concept formation appear to be associated with the amount of alcohol consumed per drinking occasion . . . even moderate social drinking is inversely related to performance on a test of abstracting and adaptive abilities."

Having established to their satisfaction that alcohol affected the ability of social drinkers to function cognitively when sober, Parker and Noble next sought to determine whether social drinking adversely affected the cognitive powers of older drinkers more than it did younger ones. Other research had established that both aging and intoxication were characterized by loss of memory, and that alcoholics also demonstrated impairment in the same cognitive processes that usually deteriorate with age. Still other investigators had suggested that alcohol has more impact on older brains than on younger ones. Alcoholics who had drunk the longest did more poorly on tests than younger alcoholics who hadn't been drinking as long. All of these findings seemed to suggest the hypothesis that "the aging brain is more sensitive than the young brain to the effects of social drinking."

To test that hypothesis, Parker and Noble reanalyzed the data they had gathered in their evaluation of the 102 California men. They divided the sample at the median age of forty-two, and then calculated the difference between the two groups in terms of the results on their tests and the amounts they habitually drank. "All significant correlations were in the direction of decreasing cognitive performance with increasing drinking and increasing age," they said in presenting their findings. "In general, these results support the notion that age and drinking affect the same aspects of cognitive performance." The reason? Parker and Noble offered a conjecture: "It appears that with increasing age, conceptual processes become increasingly vulnerable to the effects of alcohol. Older persons' reduced central nervous system tolerance to alcohol may explain the findings of the present study."*

Continuing their line of investigation, Parker and Noble turned next to young adult social drinkers. This time their subjects were 45 male students at the University of California, Irvine; they drank less often than the older drinkers previously studied, but they consumed more on each occasion. Their consumption, nonetheless—two to three drinks on the average—qualified them as social drinkers. The subjects were tested when sober; once again, their scores on standard cognitive tests were inversely related to the quantity of alcohol they habitually consumed each time they drank. Twenty-five percent of the variance in test scores was attributed to alcohol intake.

"Lifetime consumption is related to intellectual functioning because it is correlated with the amount of alcohol that subjects consume per occasion," the researchers acknowledged in a subsequent article. But, they said, "only the amount of alcohol consumed per drinking occasion significantly predicts neuropsychiatric performance." Although the performance of the students was not in the "clinically impaired range," the authors noted, "even slight losses in intellectual processes could be important to university students and to young people who are at such an important stage of their lives."†

At this point Parker and Noble were sufficiently sure of what they were seeing that they were willing to make some formulations. The hypothesis that alcohol intake was related to cognitive decrements—the notion they had originally set out to examine—was supported, they said, by findings that both alcoholics and social drinkers lost thinking power, that these powers improve when the drinkers

* *Journal of Studies on Alcohol* (January 1980).
† *Alcoholism: Clinical and Experimental Research* (July 1980).

stop drinking, and that drinking, not malnutrition, was responsible for the deficits. Two other questions, they suggested, ought to be pursued. The first was whether reduced levels of cognitive functioning led to increased drinking—the implication being that the drinkers, sensing they were intellectually second-rate, would turn increasingly to alcohol to combat their concern. The second question was whether there was some genetic predisposition or current anxiety level that leads both to more drinking per session and to decrements in sober intellectual performance.

The impact of the Parker-Noble research can scarcely be exaggerated. Both directly and indirectly, it was an attack on the "disease concept" theories that had informed social policy on alcohol in the United States ever since the end of Prohibition. That concept had all but limited the concern of researchers to the effects of alcohol, both socially and biomedically, on alcoholics. Here, now, was a scientific assertion that, for at least one potential consequence—and a critical one at that—the threshold was in the range of drinking performed habitually by millions of American drinkers.

In the following year Parker set out to accumulate still more data. Together with her husband, Douglas A. Parker, a sociologist, and Dr. Jacob A. Brody, associate director of the National Institute on Aging and a ranking epidemiologist, she investigated the drinking habits of a representative sample of 1,365 workers in Detroit—a very different socioeconomic group from those she had previously studied. Few of the subjects had been to college. Their financial resources were considerably more limited. And, for the first time, the sample included women.

The men reported that they drank an average of 1.3 ounces of absolute alcohol, between two and three drinks, on each drinking occasion, which averaged 2.9 times a week. The women drank an average of 1 ounce on each drinking occasion, which averaged 1.6 times a week. The men showed a steady decline in abstracting ability as the amounts consumed on each drinking occasion increased. Women who drank less than once a week showed no impairment; those who drank more than once a week followed the same pattern as the men—the more alcohol consumed per occasion, the greater the deterioration of abstraction abilities, i.e., the ability to see what is common or universal in things.

In September 1981 Parker reported her findings at an NIAAA epidemiology seminar:

· Light and moderate drinkers appear to experience a loss of some intellectual abilities, even when sober, as a result of their drinking.

· The degree of impairment appears directly related to the amount the social drinker usually consumes on each occasion—but frequency of drinking does not appear important.

· There may be a certain threshold frequency, or a necessary minimum number of drinking times per week before mental abilities begin to be affected—a conjecture raised by the lack of decrement in the less-than-once-a-week women drinkers.

· While the effects appear to diminish as consumption does, they are nonetheless measurable at very low non-alcoholic levels.

"We are not saying people are in the clinically impaired range, but that the subtle loss in cognitive powers could significantly interfere with everyday functioning, particularly among those involved in intellectual activities," Parker told the seminar.

Over the years, the reactions to the findings of Parker, Noble and their colleagues have ranged from approval to rejection. One study of women social drinkers by Marilyn K. Jones and Ben Morgan Jones, published in 1980 by

Rutgers University's *Journal of Studies on Alcohol,* reported that the moderate drinkers performed much more poorly on memory tasks when sober than did the light drinkers—a finding that substantiated the Parker-Noble research. The NIAAA, in its fourth report on *Alcohol and Health,* published in January 1981, appeared to take the argument a step further. "The direct toxicity of alcohol on nervous tissue, together with a chronic nutritional deficiency that often accompanies alcoholism, produces a constellation of signs and symptoms called the Wernicke-Korsakoff syndrome," the agency explained. ". . . the impairments seen in the second (or Korsakoff) stage are only the extreme end of a single scale of cognitive impairment caused by prolonged alcohol abuse; that is, heavy social drinkers, chronic alcoholics, and alcoholic Korsakoff patients are at different points along the same continuum. All suffer from the direct toxic effects of alcohol on brain tissue to a degree proportional to the amount of excessive alcohol consumption. The implication is that Korsakoff's syndrome, rather than being acute, is a progressive disease."

Citing evidence from a variety of procedures, including computerized axial tomography (known in medical circles as "CAT scanning"), researchers also suggested that chronic alcoholism can produce a significant loss of brain cells, which is accompanied by "small but significant impairment in problem-solving, nonverbal abstracting, and certain perceptual abilities"—and that social drinkers could possibly experience the same kind of impairment.

Parker insists her findings do *not* suggest that social drinking causes brain damage. "The studies involve individuals who are performing within the normal cognitive range and it is the extent to which alcohol explains normal variation that is being examined," she explained. "We are not looking at people who are performing within the clinically impaired range, as is sometimes the case with studies of alcoholic patients. The cognitive decrements being described are subtle and graded, more like those associated with the aging process, yet they may have functional significance for individuals who are engaged in cognitively demanding activities."* Another misinterpretation, Parker said, is that cognitive decrements in social drinkers are permanent. The extent to which such decrements are reversible, she noted, has not yet been investigated.†

Despite such explanations, skepticism is widespread—much of it founded on an apparent deficiency in the research method: the lack of antecedents by which to measure the supposed "decrement" of the social drinkers. "Cognitive-function studies are suspect because they don't take into account what the subjects might have been like before," asserts Walter B. Clark of Berkeley's Alcohol Research Group. "Let's say we bring a group of people in off the street and test them and we find those who drink are not as bright as those who don't. Can we say the booze made the difference? If I had to flip a coin, I'd say the studies are probably right, but there are those other factors of their past."

Among the skeptics, that is the most common sentiment: the Parker-Noble research is "probably right," but the research methods were imperfect. In 1982, however, an attack on the underlying thesis was offered by Earl B. Hunt, a professor of psychology at the University of Washington. Hunt analyzed the drinking histories and academic histories of a number of alumni volunteers in relation to their performance on a number of cognitive tasks. "The analysis indicated that there was no relation between cognitive performance and social alcohol use, after allowance had been made for intellectual performance dur-

---

* *Journal of Studies on Alcohol*, Vol. 43, No. 1 (1982).
† A study of problem drinkers at Toronto's Addiction Research Foundation indicates that abstinence or a very low level of consumption results in recovery of cognitive function, but that a moderate level of consumption prevents it.

ing the college years," a summary of his findings stated. "This data raises questions about other reports that have found a negative relation between amount of social drinking and cognitive performance. The earlier studies, however, did not control for initial level of cognitive ability."

Another, more muted attack on the Parker-Noble findings, based on a doctoral dissertation by Joy MacVane (submitted to the Graduate School of the University of Rhode Island but expanded by her and several colleagues), had been published a few months earlier.* One of MacVane's co-authors was Nelson Butters of the Boston Veterans Administration Medical Center, an authority on the Wernicke-Korsakoff syndrome. The objective of MacVane, Butters and their colleagues was twofold: first, to replicate the findings of Parker and Noble, if possible, and second, to determine whether the social drinker belongs on the same continuum with the long-term alcoholic and those with Korsakoff's syndrome.

The subjects were 106 male social drinkers from the Boston area. Their average age was forty-four; their average schooling, fourteen years. Sixty-five percent were married; 86 percent were employed. They drank an average of four times a week, consuming two to three drinks per occasion. Some of the volunteers would consume four to six drinks per occasion; they were identified as "heavy" social drinkers.

While sober, all of the volunteers were subjected to a series of tests that had been used in the past to measure cognitive problems in alcoholics. The results, the researchers reported, supported the hypothesis that social drinking "may result in negative consequences qualitatively similar to those reported for long-term alcoholics." However, they said, there was no evidence of a dose-response relationship. The heavy drinkers drank three times as often and

* *Journal of Studies on Alcohol*, Vol. 43, No. 1 (1982).

twice as much as the light-to-moderate drinkers, yet only on a vocabulary subtest was there any difference between the performance of the two groups.

Had the results of both sets of studies been influenced by the possible inclusion of alcoholics in the sample? Had the heavier drinkers in the sample consumed alcohol in the twenty-four-hour period prior to testing—in defiance of their instructions? Neither of these possibilities could be excluded because of lack of experimental controls, the researchers suggested.

"How then should the present results and those of Parker et al. be treated?" MacVane and her colleagues asked. For all the politeness and carefulness of their response it was widely interpreted as a putdown. "It is reassuring that two independent laboratories utilizing different sampling techniques and behavioral measurements have arrived at approximately similar results and conclusions. However, given the generally low correlations between drinking indices and cognitive test scores and the lack of convincing controls for abstinence prior to testing, these findings should be interpreted with caution. It would seem advisable that additional carefully controlled studies of social drinking be completed before any pronouncements concerning the dangers of social drinking are disseminated among the general public."

In her rebuttal, Parker stuck to her guns. While acknowledging the usefulness of certain of the technical criticisms, she noted that the MacVane study had independently confirmed what she and her colleagues had reported in earlier studies. "A total of five different studies have found a significant relationship between increased alcohol use and decreased cognitive performance in samples consisting primarily of social drinkers," she said. "It is becoming increasingly difficult to question the existence of the observed relationship between social drinking and cognitive performance. The challenge now is to understand it."

Pointing out that knowledge about the aftereffects of drinking was extremely limited, except for withdrawal and hangover states, Parker said: "These extreme and apparently limited states may be accompanied by subtle disorders such as cognitive inefficiency and affective disturbances. They might not be noticeable to the drinker but they could have a major influence on his capacity to deal with the stresses and strains of everyday life."

Was it, finally, a chicken-or-egg question? "Do people with poorer cognitive performance drink more or does alcohol lead to decreased cognitive efficiency?" Parker wondered. There was already evidence on the boards that teen-agers who had been hyperactive children—and who had presumably had academic difficulties—were heavier drinkers than a matched group of nonhyperactive children. But only further research would answer this and other questions.

"Research on social drinkers that initially was begun to understand CNS [central nervous system] dysfunction observed in alcoholics may eventually be relevant for a large proportion of the drinking population," Parker concluded. "By relating alcohol use to physical and psychological functioning, we may be able to gather a solid scientific basis that will allow people to make informed decisions about their drinking practices."

As to Ernest Noble, whose laboratory findings initiated the controversy, he, too, is sticking to his guns. "We all have a certain endowed capacity. Various conditions around us can compromise that," he said in the spring of 1982. "Your emotional status might compromise that; if you're worried, you're not as quick, not as sharp. Alcohol can do it; if you drink a couple of drinks a day, every day, you will compromise your faculties. You may think you're sharp. You may think you're interacting. But you're not up to par."

Perhaps because he is middle-aged himself, Noble is particularly concerned about the middle-aged drinker. The vulnerable point, he believes, is reached between the ages of forty and forty-five—the very years when professional and personal stresses are generally at their greatest, and when the individual under stress frequently begins to drink increasing amounts in an effort to ease the pressures. "What you'll have then is another burden added on to that person, which could affect his performance at home or at work. We generally pass that off and say, 'Well, he's getting older. He's not remembering so well.'" Because friends and associates tend to excuse the very kinds of behavior that result from diminished capacity, the individual whose drinking has augmented those deficiencies—particularly when he has reached fifty or fifty-five—will be unaware that they have occurred.

Noble, himself, is unwilling to take such chances. "If my cognitive stuff tells me that my social drinking is going to affect my ability to conceptualize," he says, "I'm not going to drink when I'm going to do any business. I won't drink in the daytime, even a beer for lunch. My advice is not to drink at all in situations when you have to use your high mental faculties. If I wanted to be sinister, I'd get the man with whom I'm doing business the best stuff to drink, and I'd order a Perrier water. Because I'd have the edge on that person. That's what they do in Las Vegas. It's not because they're generous that they give out all those drinks."

9 · *Threshold Drinking*

Rightly or wrongly, it has now been proposed that drinking at what has heretofore been considered a safe level might not be without impact on the health and intellectual prowess of persons who perceive themselves as social drinkers. Supposing there is something to these findings, just how much of a problem are we talking about? How many Americans qualify as "threshold drinkers"? And who might they be?

Although it is virtually impossible to generalize about the American way of drinking, certain aspects of drinking practices in this country have, in recent years, been receiving a fairly favorable press. Most Americans, according to numerous popular accounts, not only drink in moderate quantities but are substituting milder drinks for cocktails with increasing frequency and "moving beyond the hard, purposeful consumption characteristic of the Saturday night party," to quote an article in *Fortune*. Certain developments have tended to encourage such conclusions. Foremost among them is the spread of the drinking habit into the mainstream of American life, a healthy contrast to the illicit and often turbulent consumption of the Prohibition era. The increasing participation of women in American drinking rituals, in particular, has considerably softened the image of alcohol in society. Beverage tastes have changed as well. In the nineteenth century, distilled spirits accounted for 75 percent of all alcohol consumed; today only 39 percent of the total is comprised of distilled spirits; beer is by far the most popular drink, with 49 percent of the ethanol consumption; wine accounts for the remaining 12 percent. Twenty years ago, most spirits were at least 86-proof, many were 90 and some 100; today, 80-proof spirits are the rule. Wine is increasingly preferred by persons who once drank spirits. "Light" wine has been invented, following the outstanding success of light beers. And there is even a rise in the popularity of nonalcoholic cocktails, usually at business luncheons, sufficient to have warranted an article in TWA's *Ambassador* magazine called "The New No-Booze Chic."

There are a number of reasons, however, why the thesis that Americans are becoming more moderate drinkers doesn't stand up to inspection.

In the above arguments, wine is portrayed as a benign drink by comparison to spirits. In a sense that's true; table wines average 12 percent alcohol, compared to 40 percent for most spirits. What such accounts fail to mention is that a person drinking a 5-ounce glass of wine is consuming just as much alcohol as if he were drinking a standard highball.

Then there is the per capita consumption fallacy. The most impressive-seeming argument in behalf of the "moderate" American drinker is that he appears, on the basis of per capita figures, to drink so much less than people in other countries do—half that of the Portuguese and the French, 40 percent less than the Germans, 30 percent less than the Italians or the Swiss. The problem is that per capita figures don't compare drinkers and drinkers very well. When the abstainers are removed from the picture, we get a different image altogether. As Robin Room, director of Berkeley's Alcohol Research Group explains:

"While on a per capita basis the United States falls in about the middle of countries for which consumption data are regularly available, it appears that there may be only a relatively few countries in the world where alcohol consumption on a *per drinker* basis exceeds that in the United States."

Per capita consumption is figured by dividing the number of persons in the United States fourteen years of age and older into the total amount of absolute alcohol consumed. But of the 165 million Americans used in the calculation, 55 million don't drink at all, and another 40 million drink so infrequently that their consumption is of little consequence. This means that 70 million Americans are drinking the overwhelming quantity of alcohol—at least twice as much as per capita consumption figures appear to indicate, and probably considerably more. When adjustments are made for the far fewer abstainers and light drinkers in other countries, the United States—on a drinker-for-drinker basis—is right up there with the leaders.

But the most devastating argument against the "moderate drinker" image in this country is what has happened to consumption in the last twenty-five years.

Throughout the 1950s, consumption held stable at approximately 2 gallons of ethanol per person. But in 1960 it began to rise, and by 1970 it was 2.5 gallons per person, an increase of 25 percent in just a decade. Today consumption is approximately 2.8 gallons per person—an increase of 40 percent since 1960.

As we've seen, most explanations of this radical change in consumption patterns centered on the increase in women and teen-age drinkers. Subsequent analysis, however, strongly suggested that the increase was due more to increased consumption by traditional drinkers than to an increase in the number of drinkers.

Studies of drinking patterns over the same period have shown that abstention rates have held relatively steady.

Since the proportion of drinkers to abstainers in our society has remained fairly constant, the increase in consumption can be regarded as an accurate reflection of the increase in the mean consumption of drinkers.

That a profound change in the consumption of alcoholic beverages has occurred in the United States in recent years is thus beyond dispute. While changing tastes in the types and strengths of these alcoholic beverages are militating factors, they are no argument against the ultimate measure: the per capita increase in absolute alcohol consumed. The matter of how many Americans are accounting for this increased consumption, and in what patterns, is far less readily discerned. There are a number of reasons why.

The first is that even today, fifty years after the end of Prohibition, drinking in America remains a touchy and politically charged issue. There is a reticence to deal with the subject not simply on the part of the government and the public but, paradoxically, the researchers themselves. Investigations of drinking practices and their consequences are automatically suspect, and vulnerable to charges that they are neo-Prohibitionist in intent. A carry-over of this reticence about the subject can be seen in comparisons of the amounts funded for alcohol research and amounts allocated to other health-related subjects. Figures developed by the Institute of Medicine of the National Academy of Sciences showed that as of 1980, support for alcohol research was approximately one tenth of that spent on heart and respiratory diseases, and one hundredth of the amount spent on cancer research, relative to their respective economic impacts. While there is considerable disagreement as to just how much alcohol abuse costs the nation—consultants to the industry say it is nothing like the $43 billion a year or more the NIAAA says it is—even if the cost were half as much, alcohol research is clearly sucking the least productive teat.

Then, too, such money as exists for research usually goes

for research into the biomedical causes of alcoholism, one more consequence of what Don Cahalan terms "an explicit or implicit conspiracy in restraint of controversy and to divide up the spoils" on the part of the liquor industry and some of the leading alcoholism associations. "This course is non-controversial because it postpones conflicts into the distant future," Cahalan noted in his 1979 article in the *British Journal of Addiction*. "Thus expenditures for bio-medical research are vastly preferable, in the eyes of most of the alcoholism constituencies, to the spending of money on research on the political, economic and other social implications of the association between the consumption of alcohol and the problems related to that consumption."

Whatever the cause of the lack of funding, the consequence has been a good deal of gray rather than black-and-white information, as well as the production of what Cahalan refers to euphemistically as "negotiated statistics" —numbers that seem to change with the times without any real basis in research.

One of the questions that has perplexed researchers and policy makers for years is how many Skid Row alcoholics there are compared to "hidden alcoholics" still functioning, however poorly, in the everyday world. In the early 1950s, it was estimated that the traditional stereotype of the neurotic alcoholic or down-and-out bum described just under half the alcoholic population. By 1957 the estimate had dropped to 8 percent. By 1974, estimates of 3 to 5 percent were prevalent, and the NIAAA's report that year suggested that Skid Row bums accounted for "far less than 5 percent" of the alcoholic population. As nearly as can be determined, however, none of these estimates had any basis in fact. No one had gone out and counted the number of alcoholics on Skid Row; the size of the estimate had simply changed to correspond with changing perceptions of the problem.

Survey estimates of the number of heavy drinkers in the

United States are grounded in fact, but still leave much to be desired. Two criteria, both subjective, profoundly affect the outcome of the studies. Researchers establish their cut-off points, first, by what is commonly regarded as heavy drinking, and second, by the practical necessity of making certain that there are going to be enough "heavy" drinkers to study. Sample sizes are often a reflection of the amount of money available for a study. The less money, the smaller the sample, and the smaller the sample size, the more broadly defined a category must be. In a study of 3,000 drinkers, for example, if "heavy" is defined as six or more drinks a day, there might not be enough qualified drinkers to make the group acceptable by statistical standards. So the definition is arbitrarily set at five drinks instead of six.

For the user of alcohol who might want to know how he stacks up, the results can be confusing. One study in St. Louis defined a heavy drinker as one who takes four drinks a day at least four days a week, or seven drinks at a sitting at least once a week. A study on the West Coast defined a heavy drinker as someone who within the last year has drunk five or more drinks on an occasion at least once in a while. "Frequent heavy drinkers," according to a San Francisco survey, are those who drink nearly daily and have had at least four drinks a day at least three times a week on eleven or more days during the previous month. In all three instances, the "definitions" were arbitrary cut-offs designed to produce a workable sample.

Easily the most celebrated negotiated statistic in current use is the one that numbers U.S. alcoholics at 10 million. It is used almost everywhere alcoholism is discussed: by government officials, in newspaper and magazine articles, in grant applications to emphasize the seriousness of the problem, even by some alcoholism associations. In fact, the number was an accident bordering on an invention.

One day in 1970 Don Cahalan, then director of Berkeley's Alcohol Research Group, received a telephone call from one of the senior researchers at the predecessor organization of the NIAAA. At the time of his call, hearings were under way in Congress in regard to funding for the NIAAA, which was in the process of being set up. The caller explained to Cahalan that Senator Harold Hughes of Iowa, the sponsor of the bill creating the NIAAA, had asked him to come up with a "good decent estimate" of the number of alcoholics in the United States, and had given him until two o'clock that afternoon to do so. The estimate in use at the time, 3.5 million, was based on a formula that had come under attack as logically indefensible.

Cahalan had recently completed work on a book called *Problem Drinkers*, a copy of which he had sent the researcher for review. In that book he stated that 9 percent of the adult population of the United States had drinking problems—a conclusion based on survey results of a representative sample of adult Americans twenty-one years of age and over. Because the census figures in use at the time indicated that there were 100 million Americans twenty-one and older, the researcher wondered if one could say that the "alcoholic" population numbered 9 million—9 percent of the total.

The suggestion greatly disturbed Cahalan. These weren't alcoholics by any stretch, he protested. They were people who admitted to having had their share of drinking problems. Moreover, the number was an arbitrary one, projected from a sample divided into light, medium and heavy drinkers more on the basis of statistical necessity than of perceived reality.

Disappointed, the senior researcher informed his boss, who promptly called Cahalan himself. Once more Cahalan explained why the 9 percent figure could not be translated into 9 million alcoholics.

"But, Don," the bureaucrat pleaded, "you're sitting on the only figures we've got."

To Cahalan, the implication was clear. The government needed a number, and an impressive one, to make its case for a significant appropriation that would enable the fledgling NIAAA to make a dent in the admittedly serious alcohol-abuse problem in the United States. Cahalan was sympathetic to that objective—and yet he could not sanction the misuse of his figures. "I can't prevent you from making use of the figures in whatever manner you choose," he said at last, "but don't expect us to back you up."

That afternoon in Washington, the figure of 9 million alcoholics was introduced into congressional testimony. Two weeks later an assistant secretary of the Department of Health, Education and Welfare used the figure in a speech. The figure was picked up by the New York *Times*, and thereby sanctified.

Two years passed. One day Robin Room of Berkeley received a request from the NIAAA to write a section for a forthcoming publication dealing with the number of alcoholics in the United States. In conversations with NIAAA officials, and again in a subsequent memo, Room offered three numbers. If by "alcoholics" the NIAAA meant persons being treated in clinics, the number was several hundred thousand. If what the agency wished to measure was the number of persons who were currently experiencing problems with alcohol, that number was "in the order of magnitude" of 10 million. If the agency wanted to estimate how many Americans would experience problems with alcohol during their lifetime, that number was "in the order of magnitude" of 20 million.

The rounded numbers were no accident. Mindful of what had happened to the figure of 9 million problem drinkers, and recognizing that such a number sounds "spuriously accurate," Room was deliberately attempting to indicate "orders of magnitude" in an effort to make the point that these were estimates rather than precise statistics.

But in getting the story to the press, someone in the

NIAAA dropped the 20 million figure as well as the "order of magnitude" qualification, and stated flatly that alcoholics in the United States numbered 10 million. There are two versions of what happened next. One is that an enterprising reporter wrote a story to the effect that the number of alcoholics in the country had increased in recent years— from 9 million to 10 million. The other is that a member of Congress complained to his colleagues, "Look, we've been spending all this money for three years, and the problem's grown by one million."

This was not the last time the NIAAA would overstate the case in its well-meant effort to secure funds to deal with problems that would not exist if we didn't drink. A more recent example occurred in connection with the publication in 1978 of the third special report to Congress on *Alcohol and Health*. Those reports are written with the help of hundreds of consultants from all over the United States, each of whom submits a paper on a specific topic. The NIAAA then condenses those papers into a single report in lay language, and sometimes a second scientific backup report. It's the report for a lay audience that is designed to communicate the nature of the alcohol problem. For years, the liquor industry has objected to the content of such reports, maintaining that it portrays the drinking problem in this country out of all proportion to its true extent. In at least one instance, its objections are not without merit. In the material it presented to the NIAAA for inclusion in the third report, Berkeley's Alcohol Research Group expressed problems in a percentage range. A problem, it would say, affected between 37 and 77 percent of the drinking population, depending on which study one used. In its final report, however, the NIAAA would express the same idea in a significantly different way: the problem, it would say, affected *up to* 77 percent of the population. There is simply no comparing the statements,

and the Alcohol Research Group was understandably out-
raged.

Despite all the problems, a great deal *has* been learned
about how much Americans drink. The most striking discovery of all is not a number but the absolutely certain
knowledge that millions of these drinkers delude themselves
about the kinds of drinkers they are.

Over the years the NIAAA has done a number of surveys
in which it asked the respondents how much a person
would have to drink in order to qualify as a "heavy"
drinker. Robin Room later cross-tabulated those answers
against the amounts the respondents acknowledged that
they drank themselves. The basic definition that resulted
was: "A heavy drinker is someone who drinks twice as
much as I do."

"American drinking norms appear to be sufficiently
diverse and flexible for a large majority of American drinkers to define their own consumption practices as normal,"
Room's colleague, Ron Roizen, noted in a paper. Less than
one percent of the respondents in *American Drinking
Practices* perceived themselves as heavy drinkers, even
though many times that number were drinking at levels
generally conceded to be "heavy." Very few people consider their drinking unusual or excessive, according to two
recent surveys. "Taken at face value," Roizen comments,
"this finding suggests that drinking norms may be sufficiently diverse to allow almost everyone to think of himself
as a social drinker." Of 40.9 percent who labeled themselves "social drinkers" in a study conducted by the Alcohol Research Group, only half that number actually drank
small amounts of alcohol.

Survey data demonstrate unmistakably that the difference
between what Americans say they drink, when asked, and
what they actually drink is at least 30 percent, and may be

closer to 50 percent. Whenever survey results are projected onto the population as a whole, estimated volume of alcohol theoretically consumed falls far short of the amount sold in the United States each year as determined by tax revenues.

"Under-reporting of consumption patterns is not unique to alcohol," Charles Kaelber, chief of the Laboratory of Epidemiology and Population Studies at the NIAAA, and his associate, George Mills, noted in an article in the journal of the American Heart Association. "Similar observations have been made for self-reports of calories consumed and cigarettes smoked. However, the magnitude of the under-reporting appears to be substantially larger for alcohol than for these other substances. To complicate matters, it is highly probable that this apparently substantial under-reporting is not random, but is highly related to alcohol use and abuse. Those who abstain probably report this fact fairly accurately. Those who consume alcoholic beverages on only a few occasions during the year probably tend to report the alcohol use with relative precision. But those who are frequent and heavy consumers have more complicated consumption patterns and tend to be more inaccurate in their reporting.

"Further, as alcohol consumption increases, the probability of alcohol-associated problems also increases. The presence of drinking problems may diminish the desire, as well as the ability, to be an accurate self-reporter . . ."*

There are a number of reasons why the surveys themselves contribute to the underreporting. One is that they are conducted from house to house rather than in bars and restaurants, and at the time of day when the major consumer of alcoholic beverages is usually not at home. What influence that might have can be seen in the results of a test the Alcohol Research Group devised to determine the reliability of observations. They asked married men and

* *Circulation* (September 1981).

women several questions on how much their spouses drank. They then compared the responses to the spouses' own estimates of their drinking. Estimates by men of how much their wives drank dovetailed almost perfectly with the wives' own estimates of their drinking. But the wives underestimated their husbands' drinking by considerable amounts. The result, though humorous, is not surprising. Most women drink only in the presence of their husbands; most men do at least some drinking on the side.

Another problem is the general nature of the questions, which mostly have to do with average consumption. "They tell you they average two drinks a night, but they don't tell you they get totally smashed every Saturday night," one veteran survey researcher confides. Diffidence on the part of the researchers plays a part here; relative strangers, they are constrained from asking respondents how many times a week they drink five or more drinks, since such an amount is perceived as heavy drinking. And then there is the motive of the drinkers themselves; as psychologist Richard Jessor of the University of Colorado has noted, drinkers tend to answer survey questions in the most socially desirable manner, which means that heavy drinkers in particular will underestimate their consumption.

And then there is the matter of the drink itself. " 'How many drinks of vodka do you have in a day?' you ask a drinker," Kenneth Warren, a research director at the NIAAA recounts. " 'One,' he replies. But that one drink of vodka may turn out to be a fourteen-ounce water tumbler." Says Robin Room of Berkeley: "We ask our questions in terms of numbers of drinks consumed, and then we try to guess what they mean by 'drinks.' We've always tended to work on the assumption that a drink is a drink is a drink, and we've known that's a lousy assumption. We've tried fiddling with it around the edges in our survey work, but it's a very difficult task to try to get people to tell you in intimacy what they're drinking."

Because survey data are used to establish public policy, underreporting in the magnitude of 30 to 50 percent could greatly distort the nation's drinking profile and thus the government's response. But as serious as this might be, it pales beside the consequences to the individual of the self-delusion such underreporting represents.

It is eight o'clock on a windy Saturday evening in West Los Angeles. Six guests are sitting around a coffee table in the living room of their hosts, an attorney and his wife, the mother of three grown children. All eight of those present are middle-aged, and all eight are social drinkers with no past or present problems with alcohol. Three of the eight are having Scotch on the rocks, three are drinking highballs, and two are drinking wine. As the glasses empty, the host replenishes them. At eight-thirty, the hostess goes to the kitchen to put the finishing touches on dinner, a signal to the host to freshen the drinks once again. Two of the guests pass on his offer; the others take a third drink, as do the host and his wife.

Then dinner is served. With it comes a red wine. Two bottles are on the table. The first pouring depletes one of the bottles, with everyone sharing equally. The second bottle is finished before the dinner ends.

As the dinner companions return to the living room, the host offers brandy and other cordials. All but one of the guests accept; they are joined by the host and his wife. In the next hour, three of the seven nurse their drinks; the other four replenish theirs. At midnight, the guests depart.

In the course of a four-and-a-half-hour evening, one of the guests had consumed three drinks, a second guest had consumed five, two others drank six apiece, and two had seven apiece, along with the host and his wife. No one was drunk, and no one but the three-drink guest considered the amount consumed in any way extraordinary. That guest was myself, and what I found extraordinary about

the surreptitious inventory I had taken that evening was
the distance between the perception my companions had
of themselves as drinkers and the reality of their drinking.

Throughout this report I have confined myself, for the
most part, to the printed record and the judgment of
authorities. Let me now offer some observations of a reporter who has traveled extensively throughout the United
States, been a guest in scores of homes, and a patron in
hundreds of restaurants. As I write, it is approximately
eighteen months since I undertook the research for this
book. In that time I have tested many a friendship by
abruptly demanding that my host provide me with a
measuring cup so that I might know precisely how many
ounces he had just poured into his own or another guest's
drink. I have asked for and gotten confessions from dozens
of companions—and been accused dozens of times of trying
to spoil the evening. I have presented myself to the bartenders and managers of every restaurant I've visited, but
only after anonymously observing the kinds of drinks they
poured. The reportorial method is no substitute for a well-
designed survey, but given the problems peculiar to this
field, it is not without its uses.

The sociologists assure us that the kinds of drinkers we
become is as much a consequence of the social customs that
surround us as it is of our individual preferences. When
custom begins to change, we tend to flow with it, whether
we are conscious of the change or not. As individuals we
may tend to associate with others whose alcohol consumption resembles our own, but as the consumption habits of
the group changes, our own change with it. Thirty years
ago, wine was a rarity at Saturday-night dinner parties;
drinking stopped when dinner began and resumed when
it ended. Today, a Saturday-night dinner party without
wine is more the exception than the rule; drinking begins
when the party begins and ends when it ends, with no
break in between.

To a great degree, then, we drink in a manner sanctioned by our group. What I'm suggesting is that the sanctions associated with drinking in the last two decades have become considerably more expansive, so that what twenty years ago might have been called "moderately heavy" or even "heavy" drinking passes for "moderate" today.

Not long ago my wife and I were hosts to friends from Chicago. The husband, an academic, was in town on a consulting assignment, and had asked his wife to come along. On the Saturday of their visit, while he was off working, we had a picnic, at which his wife drank a glass of wine. At five o'clock she had a second glass of wine, and at eight o'clock, before we left for the restaurant to which we had invited them, she drank her share of a bottle of champagne. At the restaurant she ordered a cocktail before dinner, a Scotch on the rocks. It arrived in an eleven-ounce tumbler filled almost to the brim with ice and whiskey. Our dinner was accompanied by a bottle of Burgundy; once again, the woman drank her share. After dinner we took our guests to a favorite pub, where the woman had a nightcap, a Kahlúa on the rocks.

How much did she drink that day? The wine, champagne included, totaled 24 ounces, approximately 2.4 ounces of absolute alcohol. The tumbler of Scotch was just under three ounces, a fact I ascertained after dinner by asking the bartender to duplicate the drink for me with water. Together with the after-dinner drink, that made another 1.5 ounces of absolute alcohol, or more, for a total of at least 3.8 ounces, and probably closer to 4. At a minimum, the woman had consumed 100 grams of absolute alcohol.

How uncommon was her consumption? Typical for the weekend, she told me; untypical of week nights, when she drinks a cocktail before dinner and two glasses of wine with dinner, without fail. How typical was she of women in her community? Typical on weekends; untypical during the week, when only one in four of the women she knows takes a drink.

In all of the years I have observed this woman's husband, he has matched her drink for drink. There is one added feature to his drinking: he has a beer with lunch every day of his life.

Like the people at that party, neither of my friends had ever had any observable problems, socially or medically, as a consequence of drinking. Both considered themselves social drinkers, and neither was troubled about the amounts they consumed.

Years ago, when men did most of their drinking among men in bars, restaurants and clubs, the home consumption habits of American drinkers were not of great significance. Today, the feminization of American culture has produced a drastic alteration in drinking habits. Various survey data seem to suggest that a good two thirds of the alcohol Americans drink is consumed in the home. Willy-nilly, the size of the drink the average drinker is pouring for himself has become an important consideration.

When alcohol researchers speak of a drink of spirits, they mean anything from 1 to 1.5 ounces. Unless the amateur bartender uses a jigger—and very few do—the drink he pours himself will tend to be 2 ounces or more, sometimes 3 and, on occasion, 4.

One recent winter evening I decided to have some sherry before dinner, but not wanting to overindulge, decided to use a small glass. The one I chose resembled the long-stemmed, rounded martini glass commonly found in bars. Because of this association, perhaps, I calculated that the glass would hold no more than 2 ounces, and so, when I had finished my first glass of sherry, and dinner was still not ready, decided to have a second. With dinner, I drank a glass of wine. After dinner I was so sleepy that I went to bed before nine o'clock, bewildered at how such a small amount of alcohol could have knocked me out.

The next morning I retrieved the cocktail glass, filled it with water and then emptied the water into a measuring cup. It measured just under 4 ounces. Instead of 4 ounces of sherry, I had unwittingly consumed closer to 8. What truly discomfited me was the realization that in years past I had on occasion drunk dry martinis from these very same glasses.

A few nights later I tried a second experiment, pouring 2 ounces of gin into a cup measure, adding about ¼ ounce of vermouth and then pouring the mixture over ice waiting in a cocktail shaker. After stirring sufficiently to chill the alcohol, I transferred the martini mixture back into the cup measure. Although I had expected a considerable amount of dilution, there was surprisingly little; the liquid still measured less than 2.5 ounces. Then I poured the martinis into two of the same type of cocktail glasses I had used in drinking those two servings of sherry. The martinis I served to my wife and myself looked like no martinis I had ever served before. The glasses were slightly more than one-third full.

Numbers of researchers to whom I subsequently related my experience assured me that the drinks people make for themselves at home are often far larger than they realize. Almost no one he has interviewed uses a jigger or other measuring device, James Beard of the University of Tennessee reports. Usually they simply put ice cubes in a glass and pour. Whenever Beard proposes to a drinker that he measure what he pours, the response he gets at the next interview is almost invariably the same: "The glass wasn't even half full—and I always fill it up."

From these responses, Beard has deduced that most homemade drinks are really two drinks in one. "That's why when people go out to drink they figure that what they're being served is watered down," he observes.

And yet even commercial drinks may not be all that stingy. They vary considerably in size, but as the price of bar drinks escalates there seems to be a discernible tendency in bars and restaurants to pour a generous amount. "He told me to pour a good drink," one former bartender at Stratton's, a West Los Angeles restaurant, said of the owner, Jean Stratton. "We used very big glasses, and I poured to a quarter inch from the top." At Ben Quan's Solaris, my favorite Chinese restaurant in Los Angeles, I asked the manager, Allen Chang, how many ounces had been in the dry martini the bartender had prepared for me. "Two ounces, maybe a little more," he said. "But no one measures in Chinatown. The bartender has shot glasses but he never uses them. If you see someone measure in Chinatown, you go to another bar."

Many bartenders who do use jiggers hold the bottle over the glass and continue to pour as they empty the jigger into it. But a great many bartenders simply free-pour, using what they call a "five count" or a "twelve count," depending on their training and how fast they count. In an informal survey in bars and restaurants on both the East and West Coasts, I found that many bartenders were pouring two ounces, and in some of the more expensive restaurants, they were pouring close to three ounces.

Wine drinking in bars and restaurants reflects the same generosity. Years ago, wine glasses that held three to four ounces were fairly common; today, many bars use outsized glasses that hold eight to ten ounces—in effect, two drinks in one.

In the past, most bars and restaurants trained their bartenders to pay strict attention to the "P.C."—the "pouring cost" associated with the sale of cocktails and mixed drinks. The shot glasses in such establishments generally varied from seven eighths of an ounce to an ounce and a half. Today the "P.C." is still a concern in many bars, a good many of which control it through automated pouring devices. But many establishments, particularly those that set their sights on a brisk "happy hour" trade, appear to have determined that patrons will frequent those bars that pour a "good drink" in preference to those that don't. One restaurant, Carlos and Pepe's in Santa Monica, achieved almost instant success after opening a few years ago by serving an oversized Margarita containing 3.5 ounces of spirits. The philosophy behind such generosity is that a barkeep who gets fewer drinks out of a bottle of spirits is losing an insignificant amount of money compared to what he gains in volume from contented clients. Although the amount of ethanol consumed in bars has diminished in proportion to the amount consumed in the home, more generous-sized drinks in public establishments could account for at least some of the 40 percent increase in consumption since the end of the 1950s.

What all of these drinking patterns add up to is the likelihood that most habitual drinkers drink more than they think they do—and that many drinkers who believe they are drinking moderately aren't doing so at all. They are not "problem" drinkers in the traditional sense of the term. They seldom get drunk, and may never get into trouble as a consequence of drinking. Their problem is—or could be —of another kind: an illness related to years of "threshold drinking."

Who might these people be?

In their benchmark study, *American Drinking Practices*, Don Cahalan, Ira Cisin and Helen M. Crossley, identified a set of demographic characteristics of drinkers and heavy drinkers that defined them starkly but well:

Most Likely to Be Drinkers
Men under 45 years of age
Men and women of high social status
Professional, business and other white-collar workers

College graduates
Single men
Residents of the Middle Atlantic, New England, East North
  Central and Pacific areas
Residents of suburban cities, towns
Those whose fathers were born in Ireland or Italy
Jews, Episcopalians

Among Drinkers, Most Likely to Be Heavy Drinkers
Men aged 45 to 49
Those of low social status
Operatives, service workers
Men who completed high school but not college
Single, divorced or separated men and women
Residents of Middle Atlantic, New England and Pacific areas
Those whose fathers were born in Ireland, Latin America or
  the Caribbean, or the United Kingdom
Protestants of no specific denomination, Catholics, those
  without religious affiliation

In a series of studies following up on the findings of
American Drinking Practices, Cahalan and his associates
identified thirteen problem categories associated with drinking: heavy intake, binge drinking, psychological dependence, loss of control, symptomatic drinking, belligerence,
problems with a spouse, problems with other relatives,
problems with a job, problems with friends or neighbors,
difficulties involving the police, difficulties involving fi-
nances, difficulties with personal health.

Seventy-two percent of American men aged 21–59 reported at least one type of problem associated with drinking; 55 percent reported that the problem experienced had
been "severe." Problems were more prevalent in men aged
21–24 than in any other age group; 40 percent reported
at least one form of problem. "Dry" regions of the country
had three times as many abstainers as "wet" regions, but
dry-area drinkers tended to get into trouble as a consequence of drinking more often than wet-area drinkers.

Drinking problems were more frequent among drinkers in the lowest and lower-middle social classes than they were in the upper-middle and upper classes. "High consequence" drinking was three times more prevalent in the lowest class than it was in the upper-middle or upper class.

But those consequences are mostly forms of social disruption precipitated by infrequent bouts of heavy drinking; the affluent, well-educated urbanites and suburbanites "most likely to be drinkers" practice, as a rule, a much steadier, more ritualized form of drinking in which many of them consume four or more drinks a day every day of their lives, and mostly avoid the disruptions associated with high-consequence drinking.

Several years ago Seldon D. Bacon, former director of the Center of Alcohol Studies at Rutgers University, reported on a two-tiered study performed under the direction of his associate, Kaye Fillmore, the first part (represented by "Time 1") done in 1950 with 17,000 college students, the second ("Time 2") a 1976 follow-up on a selected 10 percent of those students. "They were overwhelmingly users of alcohol beverages," he noted. "Of the Time 1 abstainers, 70 percent became users. Of the Time 1 users less than four percent became abstainers." In the twenty-five-year interval between the first and second studies, the Time 1 drinkers reduced their consumption at each drinking occasion by between 12 and 15 percent, but in the same interval the frequency of drinking occasions increased between 250 and 400 percent. Instead of one, two or three occasions per week, the drinkers drank on five to eight occasions per week. The frenzied weekend college beer bust had given way to milder bouts of habitual drinking. Problems associated with drinking decreased 50 percent between Time 1 and Time 2.

What of long-range problems, however—the biomedical kind increasingly associated with drinking beyond the threshold? How many of these more affluent and better-educated urbanites are theoretically at risk?

Whenever a significant jump in consumption occurs—such as that we have experienced in the United States in the last twenty to twenty-five years—the proportion of heavier drinkers will increase at a greater rate than the increase in consumption. The amount everyone is drinking rises, but the amount really heavy drinkers consume rises more. For consumption in the United States to have increased 40 percent per capita since 1960 could mean that heavy drinkers are consuming on the order of 80 percent more today than they or their counterparts were drinking less than a quarter century before.

That, according to many researchers dealing with the consequences of alcohol abuse, is what has happened in the United States in the last twenty-five years, and that is why they are so concerned. When consumption rises the way it has, millions of people who might have been drinking below a safe drinking threshold rise above it.

How many? The answer to that question depends on where the threshold really is.

10 · How Much Is Too Much?

A pessimist, the old saw has it, sees the bottle as half empty; the optimist sees it as half full. Seldom has an analogy seemed more appropriate than this one to social drinking in the United States fifty years after the end of Prohibition.

No one in the world of alcohol research disputes the idea that drinking beyond a certain level is destructive to health. That world's equivalent of optimists and pessimists, however—the "problem minimizers" on the one hand, and the "problem amplifiers" on the other—not only disagree as to where the level is located, they view it from diametrically opposed perspectives. The "problem minimizers" see the level as a line to which one can safely drink. The "problem amplifiers" see it as a line beyond which dangers lurk.

To the social drinker, the conflicting advice that issues from each camp is nothing short of bewildering. Here are scientists, supposedly objective, supposedly dealing with objective data, yet arriving at recommendations that don't seem to be poured from the same bottle.

Since the researchers cannot agree even among themselves, it is left for us, the social drinkers, to sift through the arguments in an effort to determine what makes sense.

It makes sense that a small amount of alcohol, ingested daily, performs some constructive feats in the body—

cleaning the veins of substances that would clog them, making the circulatory system run more smoothly. Regardless of whatever else is involved in why moderate drinkers seem to live longer than abstainers, the ability of alcohol to increase levels of high-density lipoproteins seems a definite plus.

It makes sense that a small amount of alcohol relieves tension and thereby alleviates whatever destructive impact tension imparts, both physically and psychologically.

It makes sense that there *is* a threshold below which one can drink with a measure of confidence and above which the danger increases. But it also makes sense that this threshold is not the line it has been depicted as being but, rather, a flexible space that shrinks or widens depending on individual susceptibilities and the nature of each disease.

It makes sense that the likelihood of drinking beyond even the most widely depicted threshold has increased markedly for the habitual drinker over the last twenty-five years. That habitual drinking is simply more popular in a certain segment of society is the only possible explanation for the tremendous increase in consumption recorded since the late 1950s.

It makes sense for an individual who identifies himself as part of that social segment to compare himself to its present norms and to determine whether they are appropriate for him.

It makes sense that the chances of a long and healthy life are depreciated beyond a certain point in direct proportion to the amount that one drinks. Social drinkers who imbibe three to five drinks a day are at greater risk of an early death than those who imbibe one or two, and those who drink six or more drinks a day are at greater risk yet. All mortality tables confirm this.

It makes sense for the social drinker to determine how much he is willing to risk in reference to such odds.

There is a logic by which the possible consequences of

immoderate drinking can be virtually dismissed as irrelevant to life. The thrust of this logic is that even the worst odds so greatly favor the drinker that the risk may be below a level of concern that individuals want to deal with in calibrating their behavior.

Statistics tell us that most drinkers will not contract specific illnesses as a consequence of their drinking. Cirrhosis of the liver is the seventh leading cause of death in the United States, but the number of cirrhotic deaths in any year is only slightly more than 20 per 100,000 population for males and half that for females, and not all of those cases are associated with alcohol abuse. The "relative risks" of getting cancer of the esophagus rise spectacularly if you drink—more than forty times in some instances—but in the United States they were only 2 in 100,000 to begin with. If only a tiny minority of people who consume alcohol become ill as a consequence, most drinkers might be willing to take their chances. In terms of all the other things they have to worry about, drinking might not seem like cause for concern—and doesn't, in fact, according to an opinion survey published in the February 1982 issue of *Scientific American.* Three different groups were asked by Decision Research to rank thirty sources of risk according to their perception of how great each was. The League of Women Voters ranked alcohol sixth; college students ranked it seventh; and business and professional club members ranked it fifth.

In fact, however, alcoholic beverages are ranked second in terms of their actual annual contribution to the number of deaths in the United States. According to actuarial estimates, they contribute to 100,000 deaths, exceeded only by smoking, which accounts for 150,000.

There are several weaknesses to the logic by which drinking hazards are usually trivialized. The first is an actuarial one. The odds dramatically favor the drinker when expressed for any given year, but they are much less favorable when perceived in terms of a drinker's lifetime, particularly from middle age on, when the biomedical effects of immoderate drinking begin to show up. "Heavy drinkers don't pay for their drinking until they get considerably older," Walter Clark of Berkeley's Alcohol Research Group observes. Clark's point is that the consequences of heavy drinking often don't become apparent until well into middle age, so that any across-the-board study of heavier drinkers without regard to age would indicate only a small percentage of them with medical problems associated with drinking, whereas many of them might be in the process of developing them. Mortality tables—another way of looking at the odds—tell a more accurate story. One reason, perhaps, is that they tend to group drinkers by age and drinking experience in a much more revealing manner.

The second weakness of the logic is the nature of the comparison. Pitting drinkers against the entire population is an apples-and-oranges proposition. Only when drinkers are compared to one another can we calculate what the social epidemiologists refer to as "attributable risk." Among drinkers, in other words, how many contract cirrhosis or cancer or hypertension, or any of the other problems associated with heavier drinking? When that calculation is made, the odds worsen considerably.

The third weakness of the logic is its narrow context. The assumption is that the risk is to the drinker alone. But a casualty of drinking affects many people around him, family and strangers alike. The odds may be 2,000 to 1 that a drunk who drives his car will get away with it, neither causing an accident nor being apprehended. Millions of Americans obviously find those exceedingly attractive odds; in 1981 half of all the adults polled in a national sample confessed to either getting behind the wheel of an automobile after consuming three or more drinks or being passengers in cars whose drivers were drunk; all of them, obviously, arrived home safely. But thousands of drunk drivers who never made it home were not polled in that sample; the social and physical havoc they caused is beyond calculation.

Perceptions about drinking depend to a great extent on the position from which you view the problem, as Ron Roizen of Berkeley has suggested. "If you're looking through the window of a highway patrol car or an ambulance, drinking accounts for half the heartbreak you see on a Saturday night." A physician who deals with cirrhotic patients of whom 80 percent, according to his findings, might have avoided the illness had they drunk less than 40 grams of absolute alcohol a day will have an equally stern view of the problem. To speak of 13 deaths per 100,000 is simply not the same as saying that 31,500 Americans die of cirrhosis each year.

The fourth, and perhaps most telling, weakness of the logic is its fragmentary approach to problems associated with drinking. Ernest Noble, who freely acknowledges that looking through the window of the director's office at the NIAAA for several years profoundly affected his perceptions, considers the logic faulty principally because it deals with problems piecemeal and fails to take into account the pervasive effects of drinking. "We all inherit certain weaknesses and strengths," he notes. "There is such a thing as the family tree. When you look at your family tree, you find that a certain relative died of this disease and another died of that one. The chances are that we, too, may die from one of those disease states. The question is, 'How does alcohol accelerate the development of these disorders?' When you put alcohol into the body, it may enhance the weaknesses in those systems that are vulnerable to those diseases. You might just break down the system that's the weakest one in you. If your mother and father have high blood pressure and you're drinking heavily now, I say,

'Watch out, brother, because you're going to accelerate the development of that problem.'

"But you can't just look at the problem disease by disease. You have to look at it cumulatively, in terms of all the risks involved. Each reinforces the other, and compounds the overall risk. In order to really help yourself, you've got to consider the whole range of issues and not narrowly focus on just cancer of the esophagus and say, 'That's ridiculous. The chances are I won't get that.' All of the problems have to be dealt with and examined. When you look at all of the areas of risk together, it does begin to become impressive."

What makes it all the more impressive is the rate at which so many Americans are drinking today in contrast to twenty-five years ago. To fully appreciate how significant U.S. consumption is, let us return to those per capita drinking statistics and perform one final operation, calculating the amount of absolute alcohol consumed by habitual social drinkers.

The amount of absolute alcohol consumed in 1978, the last year for which figures are available, was 2.82 gallons, which translates to 361 ounces, or just under 1 ounce per person per day—the equivalent of two standard drinks. When we calculate that this amount of alcohol is being drunk by 110 million persons, not 165 million, the consumption figures rise by 50 percent, to 541.4 ounces per person per year, or 1.48 ounces a day. And when we adjust still further for those 40 million light drinkers, we arrive at consumption figures in the neighborhood of 2 ounces a day of absolute alcohol, the equivalent of four standard drinks for the remaining 70 million drinkers.

Not all of the 70 million regular drinkers would be consuming four drinks a day. The figure is an average. Moreover, a small percentage of those 70 million drinkers would be consuming a great deal more than the average. Could we say that half of those regular drinkers—35 million—are consuming four drinks a day? Or, being more conservative still, should we say one-third? That would be 23 million persons—still a prodigious number.

No one knows the exact answer, but an idea of what it might be can be gleaned from a cross-cultural study of drinking behavior done in Contra Costa County, California, in 1979. Where many quantity-frequency studies are compromised by vague questions and answers, this one was distinguished by the meticulous effort of the researchers to develop a day-by-day drinking diary with each subject, assisted by well-rehearsed questions to jog the subjects' memory. Asked how much alcohol they had consumed on the day in the previous month that they had drunk the most, almost half the men—48 percent—responded that they had drunk more than four drinks, and half that number had drunk well more than six. One in seven of the men had consumed nine drinks or more.

To view those new drinking patterns in terms of old assumptions *doesn't* make sense. Truly moderate drinking still seems to be a safe and life-enhancing habit, but to characterize the heavy social drinking that has become habitual in so many sectors of American life as moderate simply because it has become a norm of sorts is to give sanctity to a level of drinking that is already perceived as dangerous by a contingent of investigators.

Accepted norms aren't insulation against problems; they are often invitations to problems. It is for each person to drink not because others do and in the manner that they do, but in terms of his own perception of benefits and risks. At the very least, the drinker should understand that it is not just the deviant drinkers who have problems associated with drinking. That is an illusion fostered by America's peculiar history in attempting to cope with alcohol.

The benefits of drinking are unarguable. Alcohol does play a felicitous role in society, as well as in the life of the individual. The manner in which it diminishes stress cannot be gainsaid. It *could* be a factor in longevity. So it comes down to making certain that these and other benefits of social drinking are greater than the risks. There is only one way to do that, and that is to drink in quantities and patterns that make drinking safe.

"The effect of any drug depends mainly on the dose," Donald Goodwin, chairman of the department of psychiatry at Kansas University Medical School, reminds us. "The chance of death occurring from a sip of beer is remote. A quart of whiskey drunk in an hour will kill most men. The dose-effect rule applies to any substance a person consumes. Everything is either a poison or harmless, depending on the dose. People die from drinking too little water, and from drinking too much. A little strychnine may even be good for you (it helps rats concentrate)." Let us, then, review some recommended doses:

Dr. Thomas Turner and his colleagues at the Johns Hopkins University believe that "chronic ill effects in man are rare below a daily intake of 80 grams (just under six drinks) and thus permit upper limits of moderate drinking to be established on a more rational basis." That basis, they contend, is a weight-related formula permitting up to 80 grams per day—not to exceed three days running—for a man weighing 220 pounds, and diminishing amounts for less heavy persons. For a 156-pound person, that translates to 6 ounces of 80-proof spirits a day or its equivalent in other alcoholic beverages; for a 110-pound person, 4.3 ounces of spirits daily, or the equivalent.

At the other extreme are Drs. Pequignot and Tuyns, who have established to their satisfaction that the threshold —that point at which harm could occur—is 20 grams a day, the equivalent of 1.5 drinks, and that this threshold could conceivably be even lower. Says Dr. Tuyns: "From the work that we have done on the relative risks of esophageal cancer and cirrhosis in relation to daily intake of alcohol, there seems to be a continuous increase of risk with daily consumption. There is no neat break indicating that there might be a threshold under which one could safely drink alcoholic beverages. As disappointing as this may be, it is not biologically surprising; most biological phenomena follow that law. What can be said, however, is that there is a level of consumption below which the increase is so small that it becomes statistically impossible to scientifically conclude that there is such an increase (in cancer work, we have a similar problem with the minute exposures to radiation). Under that level, one may endlessly argue that there is, or there is not, an increase until some courageous research worker accumulates an enormous amount of observations which will demonstrate an effect for doses of 10–20 grams of alcohol per day, for example. This will not solve the question, nevertheless, because the new provisional lower 'threshold' will still leave open what happens below that level—and so on."

Can any sense be made from such totally conflicting viewpoints as those represented by Dr. Turner on the one hand and Drs. Pequignot and Tuyns on the other? Having discussed the question at some length with the parties involved, I believe that the answer is yes.

Dr. Turner based his recommendations not on original research but on a review of the scientific literature (which, inexplicably, failed to include studies of the relationship of alcohol consumption to cancer). His reasoning is best illustrated by his comments on liver cirrhosis. What he found was that most persons with the disease had been consuming approximately 150 grams a day of ethanol—better than ten drinks—for many years. A small proportion of patients with liver disease reported in the studies he reviewed drank between 100 and 150 grams. "While evidence is inadequate to permit a categorical statement that amounts below this level of daily intake do not often lead to liver damage, the data are consistent with such a conclusion," Turner wrote in part A of his two-part study.

But what if the data Dr. Turner used were incomplete and failed to include studies of social drinkers? What if no such studies existed? What if doctors, told by their cirrhotic patients that they drank four or five drinks a day, replied, "Well, that can't be the problem," and those patients, as a consequence, never entered the statistics? All of these questions were raised by Drs. Pequignot and Tuyns when I conveyed Dr. Turner's arguments to them.

In his review, Dr. Turner made note of findings by Drs. Pequignot and Tuyns that only a third of cirrhotic patients they had observed in two French districts drank more than 140 grams daily, meaning that the other two thirds drank less. "It is difficult to reconcile these intakes with those previously cited for cirrhosis," the Johns Hopkins researcher commented. That was a polite way of saying that if others hadn't found cirrhosis at lower levels, it couldn't be true. There is another possibility, expressed by Dr. Pequignot: "If others haven't found it, it's because they haven't looked. If they look, they'll find it."

The first part of Dr. Pequignot's statement is in all probability true. Until recent years, there has been almost no research into the effects of drinking at lower levels of consumption. To the scientific community, alcohol abuse was a more dramatic and more pressing subject; their investigations have, quite naturally, focused on that segment of the drinking population with habits that produce highly visible social, psychological and physical problems. But an absence of incriminating evidence that is a consequence of a lack of attention to the subject doesn't prove a thing.

Will the findings of Drs. Pequignot and Tuyns—as well as all of the others whose work has been reported in this book—be validated by replication? Who knows? Anyone who has ever worked with scientific research knows that today's revelations may be refuted tomorrow. What can be said, however, is that there is a trend throughout the field of alcohol research toward implicating smaller and smaller amounts of alcohol in adverse consequences of drinking. As these final pages are being written in the fall of 1982, a new report has appeared to the effect that alcohol, even in moderate amounts, damages the bone marrow, which in turn affects the production of red blood cells.

As the interest of researchers turns increasingly to the effects of smaller doses, investigations are likely of a number of problems that have been studied in the past only in their relationship to alcoholics and other heavy drinkers. Some of these problems are already familiar to many inveterate social drinkers. For example, even relatively modest amounts of alcohol can produce acute effects on the gastrointestinal tracts of some drinkers, such as acid indigestion, upset stomach and diarrhea. Researchers have established a correlation between heavy drinking and chronic damage in the gastrointestinal tracts of heavy drinkers, but clinicians have found lesions in the tracts of social drinkers as well. What are the lowest levels of consumption at which such problems can occur? Only time will tell.

Are the reproductive capacities of males affected by alcohol? There seems little question that drinking beyond a certain point affects testosterone levels and testicular function, but exactly what is that point? Until now only the most heavy-drinking populations have been studied, but even an informal poll among male social drinkers confirms at least the impression that their performance is affected too. Researchers have observed that the spermatozoa are just as influenced by alcohol as the rest of the body, and that sufficient quantities of alcohol will impede the ability of sperm to penetrate the wall of the ovum. Instead of bouncing about, they appear lethargic, even drunk. What is the lowest dose at which the sperm are affected—and what influence, if any, might this have on the child that results? Research may soon tell us.

There is overwhelming evidence that heavy drinking plays hob with the body's defense mechanisms—a third of alcoholics are said to die of infections—but no studies have been done at lower consumption levels. Yet one specialist in the field, Nicholas R. Di Luzio of the Tulane University School of Medicine, theorizes that even a few ounces of alcohol drunk in a brief period could impair the functioning of the body's immunological system. Host cells, under such conditions, do not migrate as well as they do normally —and it is such migration that is necessary to combat bacteria, tumor cells and virus cells.

Does social drinking rob the body of important nutrients? Researchers who have studied malnutrition among alcoholics for years are only now beginning to address themselves to that possibility.

How much of a dose does it take before one's sleep is impaired to a point that it affects one's disposition, work and health? Research has been done on this question— but only on the heaviest drinkers. Yet social drinkers know from experience that their sleep can be affected too.

Lack of evidence doesn't necessarily mean that connections may not exist between such problems and social drinking. It may simply mean that research hasn't been done yet—a point illustrated by the experience of Dr. Pequignot. "You don't have to consume at the level of physical dependence to be made sick by alcohol," he insists. For the moment at least, the evidence does seem to be tilting in the direction of that belief.

What should the social drinker who wishes to continue drinking do when confronted with such possibilities? "I used to teach my students that everyone has to decide for himself what extra risk he is prepared to take and then drink (or smoke, or drive his car, or eat, etc.) accordingly," Dr. Tuyns recalls. That seems like excellent advice.

What makes sense, if one wishes to minimize the risk, is to err on the side of caution. Truth tends to be found between extremes. To settle on a personal program halfway between the "problem minimizers" and the "problem amplifiers" would not be the worst idea—and that, in fact, is the course the most cautious of the researchers adopt themselves.

Even though they believe that the risk probably begins with the first drink, neither Dr. Tuyns nor Dr. Pequignot counsels abstinence. When I asked Dr. Tuyns—following a superb meal in Lyon during which he drank a half liter of Tavel rosé—what consumption level he would recommend, he said matter-of-factly, "Probably a formula that would accord with my own wishes." Those wishes include the consumption of approximately 30 grams of absolute alcohol a day, the equivalent of two glasses of wine, and a bit more on special occasions. Dr. Pequignot believes the best approach is to drink 40 grams—approximately three glasses of wine—twice a week. Compacting a weekly allowance of 80 grams into two drinking occasions will heighten the pleasurable effects of alcohol while at the same time giving the liver a respite from daily doses, which tend, he says, to pile insult upon insult.

Most of the researchers I interviewed in the course of writing this book seemed to agree that truly moderate drinking—a drink a day, two at most, the drinks no stronger than 14 grams of absolute alcohol apiece—did not, on the evidence, seem to be a biomedical risk. A few were somewhat more permissive. But very few of them would recommend anything higher, and there was almost no support for the levels recommended by Dr. Turner and his colleagues. What most concerned the overwhelming majority of alcohol researchers to whom I spoke was that two drinks would lead to three. To them, two drinks a day was the threshold. Three drinks was "heavy" drinking.

How much, then, is too much? Granting the wide degree of individual variability, the consensus—as far as I have been able to ascertain it on the basis of my reporting—is three drinks a day. I firmly believe that if all qualified researchers were polled on the same question, the consensus would still be: three drinks a day.

Along with drinking no more than two drinks a day on the average comes a broad range of advice:

- *Measure your drinks.* Beer is a good beverage in this regard because it's already measured. Use shot glasses when making cocktails, highballs or drinks on the rocks. Learn how many ounces your wine glasses hold, and what 4 to 5 ounces look like.
- *When you're in a bar or restaurant, remember that all drinks aren't created equal.* They can vary from ¾ths of an ounce to 3 ounces, a range of 400 percent. The person drinking at the lower end of the scale is well within a safe range. The drinker at the upper end of the scale has reached the threshold after a single drink.
- *Drink wine or beer in preference to hard liquor.* In both, the ethanol is in a milder solution. Beer, especially, gets you fuller quicker, a protection against the temptation to overindulge. If you do use whiskey, dilute it. Stay away from martinis, Manhattans, straight shots or drinks on the rocks. The less diluted alcohol is, the greater an irritant it can be; while there's no unanimity on the subject, as we've seen, spirits are usually the heavy in comparisons to wine and beer where risks to health are concerned. Says a recent WHO report: ". . . liver cirrhosis deaths rise about 50 percent more steeply with the consumption of alcohol is the form of spirits than with alcohol con-

sumed in wine or beer." Even though heavy beer drinkers have been found to have higher than normal rates of rectal cancer, beer drinkers, generally, seem to have lower mortality rates.

• *Drink when you're relaxed.* If you're uptight, don't take a drink to loosen up, because alcohol will tend to perpetuate the mood you're in. If you calm down before you drink, you'll tend not to drink as much.

• *Drink slowly.* It will help you avoid a hangover, which Paul Gavaghan of the Distilled Spirits Council of the United States terms "the most avoidable, stupid thing you can ever have." His own recommendation: one drink an hour.

• *Confine your drinking to one occasion a day.* In her study on the relationship of alcohol to mortality, Nancy Day found that men and women who drank two times a day or more—at lunch, and again at dinner, for example—had a much higher mortality rate than the rest of the population. If 1 was the mean, the rate for men who drank on two or more occasions each day was 1.7—meaning a 70 percent higher mortality. For women, the rate was 3.3—meaning a 330 percent higher mortality.

"Frequency as a measure reflected only the number of drinking occasions and not the total amount of alcohol consumed on each occasion," Day cautioned. "Combined within each frequency category were people who never had more than one drink, and those who drank considerably more on each occasion. Thus, it was possible that the higher mortality in the most frequent group was a reflection of high volume rather than frequency, or perhaps some combination of these two factors . . ."

• *Don't cluster your drinks.* If you've determined to drink no more than 14 drinks a week—two a day on the average—don't drink them all on the weekend.

"Spree" drinkers generally have significantly higher mortality rates than "standard" drinkers—four times higher according to an actuarial study made in 1950. Similar findings have been recorded as far back as Raymond Pearl.

- *Eat while you're drinking, and be sure it's something substantial.* Protein is an excellent accompaniment. Stay away from salty snacks because the salt makes you want to drink more. It's no accident that bars serve up free peanuts, pretzels and potato chips.
- *Watch your quantity.* Don't order a fresh drink just because someone in your party proposes another round. If you're a woman, don't try to match drinks with a man. Your body metabolizes alcohol less efficiently than a man's, and your liver is especially vulnerable. Also, in all probability, you're smaller, which means the same size drink will hit you harder.

If you're a social drinker who's been drinking beyond the threshold and you've decided to cut back, you may experience some discomfort at first. But you will soon be pleasantly surprised at how quickly the body adjusts. Within a week to ten days you'll be getting the same lift from two drinks that used to require four. And you can take comfort in the knowledge that damaged tissue is regenerating.

- *When you drink, enjoy it.* Many persons raised to believe that drinking is sinful drink swiftly "to get it over with." "Drinking is an enjoyable way of socializing," psychologist Alan Marlatt of the University of Washington observes, "a way of having a time out, a period of relaxation, a signal that you don't have to work right now, a letting-go experience."
- *Treat alcohol with respect.* It's a potent drug—in the view of many, the most potent of all. The difference between beneficial and dangerous drinking each day is only a few jiggers of booze.

- *Remember that drinking is not an isolated act.* It is always accompanied by a set of habits and psychological and social circumstances every one of which impinges on life in its own peculiar way. Heavy drinking could simply be a "marker" for a high-risk life style. "High" and "low" are categories not simply of drinking behavior but of human behavior as well. Drinking cannot be dealt with as an isolated phenomenon; it can only be modulated by life.

Regardless of any evidence, regardless of any advice, the choice is ultimately the drinker's. Says Ernest Noble, fifty years after the end of Prohibition: "Our job is to present the people with the facts so that they can make their own decisions. We don't want anybody telling them what to do."

Exactly.

Acknowledgments

Many of the alcohol researchers who educated me have already been cited in this book, the most effective way I know to express my gratitude. I would like, in addition, to cite a number of persons who gave me special help.

Richard Bast, director of special research of the NIAAA's National Clearinghouse for Alcohol Information, provided me with a computer search on social drinking and biomedical risk as well as scores of other leads to pertinent research.

For several weeks in the winter and spring of 1982 I virtually made my home in the library of Berkeley's Alcohol Research Group, and I am grateful to Andrea Mitchell, the group's librarian, for the grace with which she put up with my presence and my countless demands. I got to the library initially through the recommendation of Don Cahalan, the director emeritus of the research group, who encouraged, cautioned and counseled me throughout. Robin Room, the current director, was as encyclopaedic as he was patient. Ron Roizen's generosity of spirit, enthusiasm for my project, and trenchant critiques will not soon be forgotten. Walter B. Clark, Lorraine Midanik and Tracy Cameron also furnished valuable assistance.

Arthur Klatsky of Oakland's Kaiser-Permanente Medical Center was kind enough not only to share time with me but to read an early draft of the manuscript. For critical readings en route, I am also indebted to E. E. Van Brunt, M.D., director of the department of medical methods research at the Permanente Medical Group, Oakland, California; James L. Mee, M.D., Lodi, California; Morley Singer, M.D., San Francisco; and Malen Stroh, an instructor in English at San Joaquin Delta College, Stockton, California.

My thanks, as well, to Barbara Coultes at the Addiction Research Foundation in Toronto, and to Judith Wicks of the National Council on Alcoholism, for their generous help, and to the staff of the biomedical library at UCLA for unfailing courtesy and assistance.

For many years I have wanted to do a book with Robert Loomis, the executive editor of Random House. Now that I have done it, I can understand why his peers, as well as so many writers, hold him in such high esteem.

Leonard Gross

Bear Valley, Calif.
January 1983

Index

acetaldehyde, ethyl alcohol and, 27, 91
addiction, 35, 37
  dependence vs., 39
  see also alcoholism
Addiction Research Foundation (Toronto), 27
advertising, 3, 20
age:
  alcohol tolerance and, 42
  cognition and, 113
alcohol, ethyl, *see* ethyl alcohol
Alcohol and Longevity (Pearl), 51, 58
alcohol consumption:
  biological process of, 28–29
  demographics of, 3, 7, 11, 25, 114–17, 141–42
  "drink" defined in, 65–66
  ethnic patterns in, 12–13
  in home vs. bar and restaurant, 129–32
  social attitudes towards, 5, 23–24, 25, 26, 46–47, 138–41
  toxic levels of, 27–28
  see also intoxication; moderate drinking; social drinking; threshold drinking
alcohol dehydrogenase, 34

alcoholic-beverages industry, 5–6, 13, 19, 21
alcoholic hepatitis, 66, 71, 72
Alcoholics Anonymous, 10, 13
alcoholism:
  addiction and, 35, 37, 39
  biochemical consequences of, 13–14, 25–26
  dependence and, 35, 36–39
  genetic predisposition to, 42
  "hidden" vs. Skid Row, 118
  social consequences of, 22
  validity of statistics on, 119–23
alcoholism-treatment movement, NIAAA and, 18–19, 21
alcohol production, 26–27
alcohol research:
  expenditures for, 117–18
  history of, 8–10
  see also specific studies
Alcohol Research and Treatment Center (Bronx, N.Y.), 70–72
Alcohol Research Group (University of California), 11, 61, 122–23, 124–25
American Drinking Practices (Cahalan, Cisin, and Crossley), 10, 123, 132–33

psychological components in,
43–44, 46–50, 59–60
sociological components in,
43–44, 60
stress and, 44, 59
therapeutic effects of, 45
see also threshold drinking
Moskowitz, Herbert, 29

National Clearinghouse for
Alcohol Information,
98–99
National Council on
Alcoholism, 10
National Heart, Lung and
Blood Institute, 56
National Institute of Health and
Medical Research (France),
study of cirrhosis by, 73–77
National Institute on Alcohol
Abuse and Alcoholism
(NIAAA), 5–6, 18, 78–79,
117, 118, 120–23
Alcohol and Health reports
of, 5, 78, 79, 95, 108, 122
biochemical approach and,
13–16
creation of, 11–12
fetal alcohol syndrome
warning from, 94
liquor industry and, 5–6, 13,
19, 21
nervous system, alcohol's effect
on, 28, 102, 112
nitrosamines, in beer, 77
Nixon administration, 11
Noble, Ernest P., 14–22, 102–6,
107, 108, 109–10, 112–13,
140–41, 152
nutrition, alcohol and, 51, 147

Parker, Douglas A., 106
Parker, Elizabeth, 102–12
Parker-Noble research on
cognition, 102–12
Patek, Arthur J., 68–69

Pearl, Raymond, 51–52, 58, 151
Pequignot, George, 73, 75, 76,
80, 143–45, 147, 148
Pike, Thomas P. and Catherine
K., 17
placebos, 46, 47–48
"pouring cost" (P.C.), 131–32
pregnancy, 9
fetal alcohol syndrome (FAS)
in, 19–20, 90–97
fetal damage in, 5, 57
limits of drinking in, 94–95
Problem Drinkers (Cahalan),
120
Prohibition, 4, 17, 18–19, 24, 51,
114, 117, 136
public health and, 8
Repeal of, 8–9
scientific research and, 10–11
"proof," calculation of, 27
protein synthesis, alcohol's
inhibition of, 102

Repeal (Twenty-first
Amendment), 4
government reaction to, 8–9
and public health, 8–9
see also Prohibition
RNA, alcohol's inhibition of,
102
Rohsenow, Damaris J., 46
Roizen, Ron, 11, 123, 140
Room, Robin, 22, 84, 115–16,
121, 123, 125
Rosett, Henry L., 92, 96
Rubin, Emanuel, 71–72

Schenker, Steven, 97
Seattle, Wash., study of
pregnant women in, 92–94
sedatives, 99
Selzer, Richard, 67
sexual activity, alcohol and, 26,
46, 47, 48, 50
Siegelaub, Abraham B., 64, 89

About the Author

LEONARD GROSS—for twelve years a correspondent for *Look* magazine and that magazine's European and West Coast editor— has won numerous awards for his journalism, including two Overseas Press Club citations for foreign reporting, and the National Headliners Club award for general excellence. He has also authored or co-authored many books on subjects ranging from physical fitness to Wall Street to his recent book portraying the lives of the few remaining Jews in Berlin during the war's final years.

Leonard Gross lives with his wife, Jacquelyn, in Los Angeles and Bear Valley, California.